Holger Vetter
Peter Paul van Dijk

Turtles of the World Vol. 4
Schildkröten der Welt Band 4

East and South Asia
Ost- und Südasien

with a chapter on hybrid forms by Torsten Blanck

mit einem Kapitel über Hybridformen von Torsten Blanck

Vetter, Holger/ van Dijk, Peter Paul:
TERRALOG:
Turtles of the World Vol. 4
East and South Asia
Schildkröten der Welt Band 4
Ost- und Südasien
Frankfurt am Main/Rodgau 2006:
Edition Chimaira/AQUALOG Verlag ACS GmbH

ISBN 3-930612-84-4 (Chimaira)
ISBN 3-936027-92-7 (Aqualog)

Front cover/Umschlagvorderseite:
large photo/großes Foto:
Platysternon megacephalum shiui. J. Maran

smaller photo to the right/
kleineres Foto rechts:
Cuora amboinensis kamaroma. J. Maran

smaller photo to the left/
kleines Foto links:
Geochelone platynota. B. Wolff

Full page photo opposite to symbol explanations/
ganzseitiges Foto gegenüber den Symbolerklärungen:
Melanochelys trijuga indopeninsularis, Chitwan NP, Nepal. O. Born

Heddernheimer Landstr. 20
60439 Frankfurt am Main
Germany
Phone: +49-69-497223
Fax: +49-69-497826
E-Mail: frogbook@aol.com
Internet: www.chimaira.de

Publisher/Verleger: Andreas S. Brahm
Layout/Satz: Gerold Schipper
Scans: Nataliya Levkovych
Photo Editing/Bildbearbeitung: Gerold Schipper
Editorial assistance/Redaktionsassistenz: Natascha-Louise Brahm
Printing/Druck: DCM, Meckenheim, Germany
Binding/Bindung: Freitag, Kassel, Germany

ISBN 3-930612-84-4

1 2 3 4 5 6 – 10 09 08 07 06

Contents and distribution data/Inhalt und Verbreitungsangaben

Introduction

Volume 4 of the TERRALOG series is dedicated to the chelonians of the Oriental and eastern Palearctic regions. The Oriental region is a zoogeographic region that comprises the tropical parts of Asia including Sri Lanka, the Greater Sunda Islands, Bali, Lombok, and the Philippines. This region is quite sharply delimited from the Palearctic to the north, with the border following the southern slopes of the Himalayas. It corresponds to the northern distribution limits of tropical vegetation, and no chelonians exist to the north of this line. A much more complicated task is to detect the borderline between Oriental and Palearctic regions in the east of the Asian continent where faunae of both regions mix in a wide belt in the south of China. A similar situation exists in the southeast where a transitory belt that is commonly known as the Wallacea leads over in a gradual manner to the Australian faunal region (Australis); this region is also covered in the present volume (see below).

In geological terms, the Oriental region originally formed through a fusion of two separate land masses, i.e., the western Indian subcontinent that, together with Africa, Madagascar, South America, Australia and Antarctica, used to be part of the vast "southern continent" Gondwana, and, on the other hand, Southeast Asia, which has been connected to the northern continental mass for a much longer time. As far as chelonians are concerned, this composite history is evident still today, for example, by the African/ western Asian distribution of the subfamily of flap-shell turtles (Cyclanorbinae: genus *Lissemys* on the Indian Subcontinent and in adjacent Myanmar).

The chelonian fauna of the Oriental region is particularly rich in species, with the families of the Old World pond turtles (Geoemydidae) and true soft-shells (Trionychidae) being particularly diverse here. That of the eastern Palearctic is concentrated mainly in the southern parts of this region. With a center in eastern China and southern Japan, their species diversity diminishes drastically towards the north. Wallacea, on the other hand, which comprises the Lesser Sunda Islands with the exception of Bali and Lombok, but including Sulawesi and the Moluccas, forms the link between the Oriental region and the Australis. It is rather difficult to characterize as a herpetofaunistic region because numerous Oriental elements are distributed as far east as New Guinea. As far as chelonians are concerned, Wallacea is relatively deficient in specific diversity. The present state of knowledge indicates that its chelonian fauna, besides marine turtles, is limited to two species endemic to Sulawesi (*Indotestudo forstenii* and *Leucocephalon yuwonoi*), a widespread species that has its distribution center in the Oriental region (*Cuora amboinensis*), and a single representative of the Australian region (*Chelodina mccordi* on Roti Island).

Einführung

Band 4 der TERRALOG-Reihe beschäftigt sich mit den Schildkröten der Orientalis und der östlichen Paläarktis. Die Orientalis ist eine zoogeographische Region, zu der das tropische Asien einschließlich Sri Lanka, der Großen Sundainseln, Bali, Lombok und der Philippinen gerechnet wird. Die Abgrenzung der Orientalis verläuft gegenüber der sich im Norden anschließenden Paläarktis entlang des Südhanges des Himalaja recht scharf; die Nordgrenze der Orientalis ist hier mit der nördlichen Ausbreitungsgrenze der tropischen Vegetation identisch, und nördlich dieser Linie existieren auch keine Vorkommen von Schildkröten. Weitaus problematischer ist die Abgrenzung von Orientalis und Palärktis im Osten des asiatischen Kontinents, wo sich im Süden Chinas Faunenelemente beider Regionen auf breiter Front mischen. Ebenfalls schwierig ist die Grenzziehung im Südosten, wo ein Mischgebiet mit der australischen Faunenregion (Australis) besteht, das als Wallacea bezeichnet und ebenfalls von diesem Band abgedeckt wird (s. u.).

Die Orientalis entstand erdgeschichtlich aus zwei verschiedenen Teilen, zum einen dem vorderindischen Subkontinent, der ehemals mit Afrika, Madagaskar, Südamerika, Australien und der Antarktis den riesigen „Südkontinent" Gondwana bildete, und zum anderen Südostasien, das schon wesentlich länger dem nördlichen Kontinentalsockel angehörte. Dies zeigt sich auch im Bereich der Schildkrötenfauna noch heute z. B. durch die afrikanisch-vorderindische Verbreitung der Unterfamilie der Klappen-Weichschildkröten (Cyclanorbinae: Gattung *Lissemys* in Vorderindien und dem benachbarten Myanmar). Die Schildkrötenfauna der Orientalis ist sehr artenreich, eine große Mannigfaltigkeit erreichen hier vor allem die Familien der Altwelt-Sumpfschildkröten (Geoemydidae) und der Echten Weichschildkröten (Trionychidae). Die Schildkrötenfauna der östlichen Paläarktis ist vor allem auf die südlichen Bereiche dieser Region konzentriert. Vom Mannigfaltigkeitszentrum der Region – Ostchina und Südjapan – nimmt die Artenzahl nach Norden hin drastisch ab. Die Wallacea, das bereits erwähnte Übergangsgebiet zwischen Orientalis und Australis, umfasst mit Ausnahme von Bali und Lombok die Kleinen Sundainseln, daneben Sulawesi und die Molukken. Sie ist herpetofaunistisch nur schwer zu charakterisieren, da zahlreiche aus der Orientalis stammende Formen bis nach Neuguinea vordringen. Was die Schildkröten betrifft, so ist die Wallacea relativ artenarm. Nach derzeitigem Kenntnisstand beschränkt sich die Schildkrötenfauna neben den Meeresschildkröten hier auf zwei für Sulawesi endemische Arten (*Indotestudo forstenii*, *Leucocephalon yuwonoi*), eine weit verbreitete Form mit orientalischem Verbreitungsschwerpunkt (*Cuora amboinensis*) und einen einzigen Vertreter der australischen Region (*Chelodina mccordi* auf Roti).

Almost without exception, the chelonians of Asia are particularly threatened in their continued existence. Man has been "helping himself" to the natural populations in this part of the world in particular, mainly as a resource of food, traditional medicines, and to supply the national and international pet trade. This has been done for years and to an extent that left some species extinct in the wild in some countries or even throughout their original distribution ranges. It must be feared that other species will follow on this path to doom, and others may have disappeared for ever before science even took notice of their existence. Many a form of Asian chelonian probably owes the fact that it still exists only to the engagement of zoological gardens and experienced private enthusiasts all over the world who have dedicated themselves to keeping them alive and propagating them in captivity and thus provide specimens that may be used for repopulation projects in suitable and protected natural habitats. It is to be hoped that the relatively recent endeavors to conserve these forms of chelonians will take effect in a rapid and efficient manner so that the present volume of TERRALOG will not need to be subtitled with "Once upon a time, there were ..." in just a few years, but can continue to serve as a documentation of beauty and diversity of still existing representatives of this fascinating group of animals.

By and large, I am following the systematics according to IVERSON (1992), with most of the differences resulting from more recent findings and descriptions published since 1992. The latter will not be discussed in detail, but the other differences are going to be explained in the following lines:

First of all, it must be stated that the systematics applied in this text have been simplified to a considerable degree. "Modern" systematic lists frequently make use of numerous intermediate categories such as infraorders, super- and subfamilies, genus groups etc., which partially result from the inclusion of extinct chelonians in those lists. These categories may be justified, but they are not considered herein in favor of a simplified systematic scheme which is easier to overview as well. Consequently, the families, genera and species are presented in a purely alphabetical order (except the marine species), even if this sequence does not always reflect the real systematic relationships.

In the course of preparing this book, the co-authors discussed various complex issues regarding the systematics of Asian turtles. We have agreed to disagree on various details, and the nomenclature used in this volume is that favoured by the senior author.

Gerade die Schildkröten Asiens sind heute fast ausnahmslos stark in ihrem Fortbestand bedroht. Der Mensch „bedient" sich der natürlichen Bestände vor allem in diesem Teil der Welt aus verschiedenen Gründen (Verzehr, traditionelle Medizin, nationaler und internationaler Tierhandel) seit Jahren in einem Maße, dass manche Arten bereits in einzelnen Ländern oder in ihrem gesamten Verbreitungsgebiet als in der Natur ausgestorben gelten müssen. Es steht zu befürchten, dass weitere Arten auf diesem Wege folgen werden und andere bereits unwiederbringlich verschwunden sind, bevor die Wissenschaft überhaupt Kenntnis von deren Existenz erlangte. So manche asiatische Schildkrötenform verdankt die Tatsache ihres Überlebens wahrscheinlich nur dem engagierten Einsatz von Zoos und erfahrenen Privathaltern aus aller Welt, die sich den Erhalt dieser Tiere in menschlicher Obhut zum Ziel gesetzt haben, um die Nachzuchten zukünftig Wiederansiedlungsprojekten in geeigneten, geschützten Lebensräumen zur Verfügung stellen zu können. Es steht zu hoffen, dass die noch relativ jungen Bemühungen um die Erhaltung dieser Schildkrötenformen ebenso schnell wie wirksam greifen werden, damit der vorliegende TERRALOG-Band nicht bereits in wenigen Jahren den Untertitel „es war einmal" tragen muss, sondern weiterhin als Dokumentation der Schönheit und der Variabilität nach wie vor existierender Vertreter dieser faszinierenden Tiergruppe dienen kann.

Ich folge hier im Großen und Ganzen der Systematik von IVERSON (1992), wobei die meisten Abweichungen aus neuen Erkenntnissen und Neubeschreibungen resultieren, die seit 1992 vorliegen. Auf letztere soll hier nicht weiter eingegangen werden. Die sonstigen Unterschiede seien nachfolgend erläutert:

Zunächst sei festgestellt, dass die hier verwendete Systematik stark vereinfacht dargestellt wurde. In „moderneren" systematischen Listen tauchen zusätzlich noch zahlreiche Zwischenkategorien wie Zwischenordnungen, Über- und Unterfamilien, Gattungsgruppen usw. auf, die z. T. daraus resultieren, dass ausgestorbene Schildkrötengruppen mit in die Listen aufgenommen wurden. Diese Kategorien mögen auch ihre Berechtigung haben, doch soll hier zugunsten einer vereinfachten, übersichtlichen Systematik auf sie verzichtet werden. Daher wurde mit Ausnahme der Meeresschildkröten bei der Reihenfolge der Familien, Gattungen und Arten eine rein alphabetische Abfolge gewählt, die nicht immer den tatsächlichen verwandtschaftlichen Verhältnissen entspricht.

Während der Vorbereitung dieses Bandes diskutierten wir diverse systematische Fragestellungen, kamen jedoch nicht in allen Punkten zu derselben Meinung. Die hier vorgelegte Nomenklatur spiegelt die Ansichten des Erstautors wider.

Family Cheloniidae

Genus *Chelonia*: As in almost every genus of the Cheloniidae, the taxonomic status of the different populations of Green sea turtles is extremely controversial. Whereas most scientists recognize only one species, *Chelonia mydas*, others – e.g. IVERSON (1992) – accept *Chelonia agassizii* as a second species of this genus. Studies like those published by BOWEN *et al.* (1992) have shown that certain genetic and morphological differences exist between the Atlantic and Pacific populations. Accordingly, the recognition of an Atlantic (*Chelonia mydas mydas*) and an Indopacific (*Chelonia mydas japonica*) seems justified. On the other hand, KARL & BOWEN (1999) and other authors were unable to confirm the specific status of *Chelonia agassizii* by means of genetic analyses. With respect to the minimal external differences existing between Eastern Pacific and Atlantic and Western Pacific Green sea turtles, it may even be doubted whether *Chelonia agassizii* deserves recognition as a subspecies. According to KARL & BOWEN (1999), the Eastern Pacific Green sea turtle can be defined as an own taxon only by geographic or political arguments (species protection). In view of these arguments, *agassizii* is recognized here as a third subspecies of *Chelonia mydas* (besides *Chelonia m. mydas* and *C. m. japonica*). However, in southern and eastern Asia, only *C. m. japonica* is distributed.

Family Geoemydidae

Following GAFFNEY & MEYLAN (1988), the Old world pond turtles (including the Central and South American genus *Rhinoclemmys*) today are almost universally regarded as a valid family, and not as a subfamily of the Emydidae. In the current literature, the name Bataguridae (as based on Batagurina GRAY, 1869) is usually applied to this family. However, BOUR & DUBOIS (1986) showed that Geoemydidae THEOBALD, 1868 is an older name coined one year earlier. Although FRITZ (2001) pleaded against a strict application of the rule of priority in this case, so that the family name Bataguridae would – in favor of taxonomic stability – remain valid according to the intention of the fourth edition of the *International Code of Zoological Nomenclature* (ICZN 1999), it must be stated that Old world pond turtles are regarded as a separate family only since the late 1980s, a period too short to warrant general acceptance of the term Bataguridae, which would be the only acceptable argument against the strict application of the rule of priority.

Familie Cheloniidae

Gattung *Chelonia*: Die Arten- und Unterartenfrage bei den Suppenschildkröten ist wie bei fast allen Cheloniidae äußerst umstritten. Während manche Autoren nur eine Art (*Chelonia mydas*) anerkennen, führen andere, so auch IVERSON (1992), *C. agassizii* als zweite Art auf. Mehrere Untersuchungen, z. B. von BOWEN *et al.* (1992), zeigten, dass zwischen atlantischen und pazifischen Populationen tatsächlich gewisse genetische und morphologische Unterschiede existieren. Es erscheint so gerechtfertigt, zumindest eine atlantische (*C. m. mydas*) und eine indopazifische Unterart (*C. m. japonica*) zu unterscheiden. KARL & BOWEN (1999) konnten ebenso wie andere Autoren den Artstatus von *C. agassizii* durch genetische Untersuchungen nicht bestätigen; die geringen äußerlichen Unterschiede zwischen ostpazifischen Suppenschildkröten einerseits und ihren atlantischen und westpazifischen Artgenossen andererseits lassen selbst den Status einer Unterart für *agassizii* ungerechtfertigt erscheinen. Allenfalls geographische und naturschutzpolitische Argumente sprechen nach KARL & BOWEN (1999) für die Einstufung der ostpazifischen Suppenschildkröten als eigenständiges Taxon. Ich trage diesen Argumenten hier Rechnung, indem ich *agassizii* zumindest vorerst nur als dritte Unterart neben *mydas* und *japonica* anerkenne, die allerdings ebenso wie die Nominatform in Süd- und Ostasien nicht verbreitet ist.

Familie Geoemydidae

Die Sumpfschildkröten der Alten Welt (zuzüglich der mittel- und südamerikanischen Gattung *Rhinoclemmys*) bilden nach nunmehr fast einhelliger Auffassung, GAFFNEY & MEYLAN (1988) folgend, eine eigenständige Familie und keine Unterfamilie der Emydidae. Für diese Familie wird in der Literatur meist der Name Bataguridae (basierend auf Batagurina GRAY, 1869) verwendet. BOUR & DUBOIS (1986) wiesen jedoch darauf hin, dass mit Geoemydidae THEOBALD, 1868 eine um ein Jahr ältere Bezeichnung existiert. FRITZ (2001) plädierte zwar dafür, die Prioritätsregel in diesem Fall nicht strikt anzuwenden und den Namen Bataguridae gemäß der Intention der 4. Auflage des *International Code of Zoological Nomenclature* (ICZN, 1999) zur Wahrung der Stabilität der zoologischen Namensgebung für diese Familie beizubehalten, doch werden die Altwelt-Sumpfschildkröten erst seit Ende der 1980er-Jahre regelmäßig als eigenständige Familie angesehen; dieser Zeitraum ist jedoch zu kurz, als dass der Gebrauch der Bezeichnung Bataguridae eine solche Stabilität erreicht haben könnte, dass ihr Erhalt über die strikte Anwendung der Prioritätsregel gestellt werden könnte.

Genus *Cathaiemys*: The species contained in this genus have previously been treated as *Mauremys*. However, according to BARTH *et al.* (2004) and others, the species *annamensis* and *mutica* represent a distinct clade within the "traditional" genus *Mauremys*. In contrast to these authors it is granted the rank of a genus here, because the concept of a "supergenus *Mauremys*", as suggested by BARTH *et al.* (2004) and promoted by SPINKS *et al.* (2004) as well as FELDMAN & PARHAM (2004) that would also include the genera *Cathaiemys*, *Chinemys* and *Ocadia* recognized as valid here (in addition to the European/North African/western Asian genera *Emmenia* and *Mauremys*), appears to me as too far-reaching. The only other alternative would be, as has been indicated by BARTH *et al.* (2004) and is promoted here, to maintain the genera *Chinemys* and *Ocadia* and split the former genus *Mauremys* into further genera. *Mauremys* in a strict sense is therefore limited to its type species, i.e., *Mauremys leprosa* from the Iberian Peninsula and North Africa. Previously included in the *Cathaiemys mutica* group were the "species" "*Mauremys iversoni* PRITCHARD & MCCORD, 1991" and "*Mauremys pritchardi* MCCORD, 1997", but as WINK *et al.* (2001) discovered, these were actually hybrids between *Cathaiemys mutica* and *Pyxiclemmys trifasciata* and *Chinemys reevesii*, respectively. As far as "*Mauremys iversoni*" was concerned, PARHAM *et al.* (2001) arrived at the same conclusion. These two "species" are therefore not regarded as separate taxa here, but dealt with in the chapter on hybrids. The genetic studies conducted by HONDA *et al.* (2002), on the other hand, suggested that "*Mauremys iversoni*" would be most closely related to *Cathaiemys annamensis*, which might indicate that the name "*Mauremys iversoni*" in actual fact comprises more than two different parental forms.

Genus *Chinemys*: In contrast to SPINKS *et al.* (2004), *Chinemys* is maintained here as a valid genus (also see the explanation under Genus *Cathaiemys*). The specific status of *Chinemys megalocephala* was disputed by IVERSON *et al.* (1989) and the name relegated to the synonymy of *Chinemys reevesii*. Chromosomal studies by GUO *et al.* (1997) showed, however, distinct differences between the two forms. The latest genetic study by BARTH *et al.* (2003) again revealed no different expressions in the mitochondrial DNA of *Chinemys megalocephala* and *Chinemys reevesii*, but these authors thought further genetic investigations would be required to conclusively evaluate the status of *Chinemys megalocephala*. It is for this reason that I have preliminarily included *Chinemys megalocephala* in my list of valid species here. The distributional data for the species of the genus follow those given by MCCORD & JOSEPH-OUNI (2004).

Gattung *Cathaiemys*: Die zu dieser Gattung gestellten Arten wurden bislang unter *Mauremys* geführt. Die beiden Arten *annamensis* und *mutica* stellen jedoch u. a. nach BARTH *et al.* (2004) innerhalb der „alten" Gattung *Mauremys* eine abgrenzbare Verwandtschaftsgruppe dar, der hier im Unterschied zu diesen Autoren Gattungsrang eingeräumt wird, da das von BARTH *et al.* (2004) angedeutete und von SPINKS *et al.* (2004) und FELDMAN & PARHAM (2004) vertretene Konzept einer „Großgattung *Mauremys*", die die hier anerkannten Gattungen *Cathaiemys*, *Chinemys* und *Ocadia* (und die europäisch-nordafrikanisch-westasiatischen Gattungen *Emmenia* und *Mauremys*) in sich vereinigt, meiner Ansicht nach zu weitreichend ist. Die einzige andere Alternative ist die auch von BARTH *et al.* (2004) diskutierte und hier vertretene Möglichkeit, die Gattungen *Chinemys* und *Ocadia* beizubehalten und die bisherige Gattung *Mauremys* in weitere Gattungen aufzuspalten. *Mauremys* im engeren Sinne umfasst demnach nur noch die Typusart *Mauremys leprosa* von der Iberischen Halbinsel und aus Nordafrika. Die früher zur Verwandtschaftsgruppe von *Cathaiemys mutica* gezählten „Arten" „*Mauremys iversoni* PRITCHARD & MCCORD, 1991" und „*Mauremys pritchardi* MCCORD, 1997" sind nach Erkenntnissen von WINK *et al.* (2001) Hybriden zwischen *Cathaiemys mutica* einerseits und *Pyxiclemmys trifasciata* bzw. *Chinemys reevesii* andererseits. PARHAM *et al.* (2001) kamen bezüglich „*Mauremys iversoni*" zum gleichen Ergebnis. Aus diesem Grunde werden diese beiden „Arten" hier nicht als eigenständige Taxa angesehen, sondern im Kapitel über Hybriden behandelt. HONDA *et al.* (2002) kamen allerdings nach ihren genetischen Untersuchungen zu dem Ergebnis, dass „*Mauremys iversoni*" am nächsten mit *Cathaiemys annamensis* verwandt ist; möglicherweise verbergen sich unter der Bezeichnung „*Mauremys iversoni*" sogar mindestens zwei verschiedene Schildkrötenformen.

Gattung *Chinemys*: Im Unterschied zu SPINKS *et al.* (2004) wird *Chinemys* hier als Gattung beibehalten, siehe auch Erläuterungen zur Gattung *Cathaiemys*. Der Artstatus von *Chinemys megalocephala* wurde von IVERSON *et al.* (1989) bestritten, die diese Form als Synonym von *Chinemys reevesii* ansahen. GUO *et al.* (1997) fanden bei ihren Chromosomenuntersuchungen jedoch deutliche Unterschiede zwischen beiden Formen. Die neueste genetische Untersuchung von BARTH *et al.* (2003) erbrachte wiederum keine unterschiedlichen Ausprägungen in der mitochondrialen DNA von *Chinemys megalocephala* und *Chinemys reevesii*, diese Autoren halten für die endgültige Klärung des Status von *Chinemys megalocephala* aber weitere genetische Untersuchungen für erforderlich. Aus diesem Grund habe ich *Chinemys megalocephala* hier vorläufig mit in meine Liste übernommen. Die Verbreitungsangsaben zu den Arten dieser Gattung folgen MCCORD & JOSEPH-OUNI (2004).

Genus *Cistoclemmys*: see also the annotations on the genus *Cuora*. "*Cuora serrata*" was originally defined as a subspecies of *Cistoclemmys galbinifrons* by IVERSON & McCORD (1992), but subsequently elevated to species rank by FRITZ & OBST (1997). However, more recent studies by PARHAM *et al.* (2001) suggested it to be merely a bastard form between *Cistoclemmys bourreti, C. galbinifrons, C. picturata* and *Pyxidea mouhotii.* It is therefore not regarded as a separate taxon here, but dealt with in the chapter on hybrids instead.

Genus *Cuora*: HONDA *et al.* (2002), STUART & PARHAM (2004) and SPINKS *et al.* (2004) referred the generic names *Cistoclemmys* GRAY, 1863 and *Pyxidea* GRAY, 1863 to the synonymy of *Cuora*, but I have opted here to follow IVERSON (pers. comm.), who regards these two groups as well as *Pyxiclemmys* GRAY, 1863, as monophyletic clusters, each of which is deserving of a separate generic status.

Genus *Cyclemys*: The systematics of this genus are largely based on GUICKING *et al.* (2002), but I agree with ARTNER (2003) in regarding the populations on Borneo as a separate species, *Cyclemys ovata*. *Cyclemys pulchristriata* is classified as a subspecies of *Cyclemys atripons* here (IVERSON pers. comm.).

Genus *Geoemyda*: *Geoemyda japonica* was for a long time treated as a subspecies of *Geoemyda spengleri*, until YASUKAWA *et al.* (1992) elevated it to species level. The taxon *silvatica,* which used to be assigned to the genus *Geoemyda* has recently been placed into the genus *Vijayachelys* (PRASCHAG *et al.* 2006).

Genus *Heosemys*: See also the annotations on the genera *Geoemyda*, *Leucocephalon* and *Siebenrockiella*. According to the results published by SPINKS *et al.* (2004), *Hieremys annandalii* might also be placed in *Heosemys*.

Genus *Kachuga*: The species content follows DAS (2001); see also the annotations on the genus *Pangshura*.

Genus *Leucocephalon*: McCORD *et al.* (1995) originally placed their new species *yuwonoi* in the genus *Geoemyda*. FRITZ & OBST (1996) then recommended maintaining this species in *Heosemys* until further research results became available, but McCORD *et al.* (2000) demonstrated that a separate genus for *yuwonoi* would be warranted.

Genus *Ocadia*: *Ocadia japonica* used to be included in the genus *Mauremys*, but the results published by SPINKS *et al.* (2004) and FELDMAN & PARHAM (2004) suggest it to be more closely related to *Ocadia sinensis*. It is likely to be deserving of a genus of its own (IVERSON pers. comm.). "*Ocadia glyphistoma* McCORD & IVERSON, 1994" and "*Ocadia philippeni* McCORD & IVERSON, 1992" appear to be hybrid forms, i.e., between *Ocadia*

Gattung *Cistoclemmys*: Siehe auch Erläuterungen zur Gattung *Cuora*. „*Cuora serrata*" wurde ursprünglich von IVERSON & McCORD (1992) als Unterart von *Cistoclemmys galbinifrons* beschrieben, doch erhoben sie FRITZ & OBST (1997) in den Artrang; neueren Erkenntnissen von PARHAM *et al.* (2001) zufolge stellt sie allerdings nur eine Bastardform aus *Cistoclemmys bourreti, C. galbinifrons, C. picturata* und *Pyxidea mouhotii* dar. Aus diesem Grunde wird diese „Art" hier nicht als eigenständiges Taxon angesehen, sondern im Kapitel über Hybriden behandelt.

Gattung *Cuora*: HONDA *et al.* (2002), STUART & PARHAM (2004) und SPINKS *et al.* (2004) stellten die Gattungsnamen *Cistoclemmys* GRAY, 1863 und *Pyxidea* GRAY, 1863 in die Synonymie von *Cuora*, doch folge ich hier IVERSON (pers. Mittlg.), nach dessen Auffassung sowohl diese beiden Formenkreise als auch *Pyxiclemmys* GRAY, 1863 jeweils monophyletische Gruppen darstellen, denen Gattungsstatus eingeräumt werden sollte.

Gattung *Cyclemys*: Die Systematik dieser Gattung folgt überwiegend GUICKING *et al.* (2002), doch bin ich mit ARTNER (2003) der Ansicht, dass die Populationen auf Borneo eine eigenständige Art, *Cyclemys ovata*, darstellen. *Cyclemys pulchristriata* wird als Unterart von *Cyclemys atripons* eingestuft (pers. Mittlg. IVERSON).

Gattung *Geoemyda*: *Geoemyda japonica* wurde lange Zeit als Unterart von *Geoemyda spengleri* angesehen, von YASUKAWA *et al.* (1992) aber in den Artrang erhoben. Die bislang häufig zu *Geoemyda* gerechnete Art *silvatica* wurde mittlerweile in eine monotypische Gattung *Vijayachelys* überführt (PRASCHAG *et al.* 2006).

Gattung *Heosemys*: Siehe auch Erläuterungen zu den Gattungen *Geoemyda*, *Leucocephalon* und *Siebenrockiella*. *Hieremys annandalii* ist nach den Studienergebnissen von SPINKS *et al.* (2004) möglicherweise ebenfalls zu *Heosemys* zu stellen.

Gattung *Kachuga*: Artenumfang nach DAS (2001). Siehe auch Erläuterungen zur Gattung *Pangshura*.

Gattung *Leucocephalon*: McCORD *et al.* (1995) stellten die von ihnen beschriebene Art *yuwonoi* ursprünglich zur Gattung *Geoemyda*. FRITZ & OBST (1996) empfahlen, diese Art bis zum Vorliegen weiterer Ergebnisse zumindest vorläufig in *Heosemys* einzugruppieren, doch zeigten McCORD *et al.* (2000), dass der Rang einer eigenen Gattung für *yuwonoi* gerechtfertigt erscheint.

Gattung *Ocadia*: *Ocadia japonica* wurde bislang zur Gattung *Mauremys* gestellt, ist nach den Erkenntnissen von SPINKS *et al.* (2004) und FELDMAN & PARHAM (2004) jedoch näher mit *Ocadia sinensis* verwandt. Wahrscheinlich gebührt ihr der Status einer eigenständigen Gattung (pers. Mittlg. IVERSON). Bei „*Ocadia glyphistoma* McCORD & IVERSON, 1994" und „*Ocadia philippeni* McCORD & IVERSON, 1992" handelt es sich

sinensis on the one, and *Cathaiemys annamensis* and *Pyxiclemmys trifasciata*, respectively, on the other hand. For this reason they are not treated as separate taxa here, but dealt with in the chapter on hybrids.

Genus *Panayaenemys*: DIESMOS *et al.* (2005) introduced this taxon as a subgenus of *Siebenrockiella*, exclusively for the species "*Siebenrockiella leytensis*", but I here accept it at generic level.

Genus *Pangshura*: Originally resurrected as a subgenus of *Kachuga* by MOLL (1985, 1986, 1987), *Pangshura* was elevated to genus level by DAS (2001). In treating *Pangshura flaviventer* as a species in its own right and not as a subspecies of *Pangshura tentoria*, I follow SCHLEICH & KÄSTLE (2002).

Genus *Pyxiclemmys*: See annotations on the genus *Cuora*. *Pyxiclemmys aurocapitata* is now regarded as a subspecies of *Pyxiclemmys pani* (BLANCK & TANG 2005).

Genus *Pyxidea*: See annotations on the genus *Cuora*.

Genus *Sacalia*: "*Sacalia pseudocellata* IVERSON & MCCORD, 1992" appears to be a hybrid form involving *Sacalia quadriocellata* and *Pyxiclemmys trifasciata*. It is therefore not regarded as a separate taxon, but dealt with in the chapter on hybrids.

Genus *Vijayachelys*: PRASCHAG *et al.* (2006) placed the taxon *silvatica* in its monotypic genus, *silvatica* had previously been considered a member of the genus *Geoemyda*.

Family Platysternidae

Genus *Platysternon*: The recognition of only three subspecies of the Big-headed turtle follows ERNST & LAEMMERZAHL (2002).

Family Testudinidae

Genus *Geochelone*: The generic concept promoted here in accordance with, for example, BOUR (1980, 1985), GERLACH (2001), BOUR (2004), PHILIPPEN (2004) and IVERSON (pers. comm.) leaves this genus only with the species *elegans* and *platynota*.

Genus *Indotestudo*: *Indotestudo travancorica* was for a long time regarded as a synonym of *Indotestudo forstenii*, but is in fact a separate species according to the findings by PRITCHARD (2000) and IVERSON *et al.* (2001).

Family Trionychidae

Genus *Oscaria*: I have opted here to follow the suggestion by BOUR & PRITCHARD (in DAVID [1994]) that the species *swinhoei* be removed from the apparently "artificial" genus *Rafetus* and placed in a genus of its own. The species *Rafetus leloii* HÀ DÌNH DÚC, 2000, described from Vietnam is identical with *Oscaria swinhoei* according to FARKAS & WEBB (2003).

offenbar um Hybridformen, und zwar zwischen *Ocadia sinensis* einerseits und *Cathaiemys annamensis* bzw. *Pyxiclemmys trifasciata* andererseits. Aus diesem Grunde werden diese beiden „Arten" hier nicht als eigenständige Taxa angesehen, sondern im Kapitel über Hybriden behandelt.

Gattung *Panayaenemys*: DIESMOS *et al.* (2005) schufen dieses Taxon als Untergattung (einzige Art: „*Siebenrockiella leytensis*") von *Siebenrockiella*, doch erkenne ich ihm Gattungsstatus zu.

Gattung *Pangshura*: Ursprünglich von MOLL (1985, 1986, 1987) als Untergattung von *Kachuga* „wiedererweckt", wurde *Pangshura* von DAS (2001) in den Gattungsrang erhoben. Die Einstufung von *Pangshura flaviventer* als eigenständige Art und nicht als Unterart von *Pangshura tentoria* folgt SCHLEICH & KÄSTLE (2002).

Gattung *Pyxiclemmys*: Siehe Erläuterungen zur Gattung *Cuora*. *Pyxiclemmys aurocapitata* wird als Unterart von *Pyxiclemmys pani* eingestuft (BLANCK & TANG 2005).

Gattung *Pyxidea*: Siehe Erläuterungen zur Gattung *Cuora*.

Gattung *Sacalia*: Bei „*Sacalia pseudocellata* IVERSON & MCCORD, 1992" handelt es sich offenbar um eine Hybridform zwischen *Sacalia quadriocellata* und *Pyxiclemmys trifasciata*. Aus diesem Grunde wird diese „Art" hier nicht als eigenständiges Taxon angesehen, sondern im Kapitel über Hybriden behandelt.

Gattung *Vijayachelys*: In diese monotypische Gattung stellen PRASCHAG *et al.* (2006) die bislang meist zur Gattung *Geoemyda* gerechnete Art *silvatica*.

Familie Platysternidae

Gattung *Platysternon*: Die Anerkennung von nur drei Unterarten der Großkopfschildkröte folgt ERNST & LAEMMERZAHL (2002).

Familie Testudinidae

Gattung *Geochelone*: Nach dem hier vertretenen Gattungskonzept nach z. B. BOUR (1980, 1985), GERLACH (2001), BOUR (2004), PHILIPPEN (2004) und IVERSON (pers. Mittlg.) umfasst diese Gattung nur die Arten *elegans* und *platynota*.

Gattung *Indotestudo*: *Indotestudo travancorica* wurde lange Zeit als Synonym von *Indotestudo forstenii* angesehen, doch stellen beide Formen nach Erkenntnissen von PRITCHARD (2000) und IVERSON *et al.* (2001) eigenständige Arten dar.

Familie Trionychidae

Gattung *Oscaria*: Ich folge hier der Anregung von BOUR & PRITCHARD (in DAVID [1994]), löse die Art *swinhoei* aus der wohl „künstlichen" Gattung *Rafetus* heraus und stelle sie in eine eigene Gattung. Die aus Vietnam beschriebene Art *Rafetus leloii* HÀ DÌNH DÚC, 2000 ist nach FARKAS & WEBB (2003) mit *Oscaria swinhoei* identisch.

Genus *Pelochelys*: Webb (1995) has demonstrated that *Pelochelys cantorii* is a good species and not a synonym of *Pelochelys bibroni*, which leaves the latter restricted to the south of New Guinea.

Genus *Pelodiscus*: According to Chkhikvadze (1987) as well as Fritz & Obst (1999), *Pelodiscus maackii* represents a species, or at least a subspecies, that is clearly distinct from *Pelodiscus sinensis*. The status of *Pelodiscus axenaria* (Zhou, Zhang & Fang, 1991) and *Pelodiscus parviformis* Tang, 1997 are unclear at present. While the former name is likely to be based on juveniles of *Pelodiscus sinensis* according to Zhao (1997), the latter is poorly defined. If both should indeed turn out to be good species, it is very likely that older names exist in the very long list of synonyms for *Pelodiscus sinensis* (Fritz & Obst 1999). It is for this reason that both "species" are not dealt with here any further, pending further research results.

Gattung *Pelochelys*: Webb (1995) zeigte, dass *Pelochelys cantorii* eine eigenständige Art und kein Synonym der nunmehr auf den Süden Neuguineas beschränkten *Pelochelys bibroni* ist.

Gattung *Pelodiscus*: *Pelodiscus maackii* stellt laut Chkhikvadze (1987) sowie Fritz & Obst (1999) eine eigenständige, deutlich von *Pelodiscus sinensis* unterscheidbare Art oder zumindest Unterart dar. Der Status von *Pelodiscus axenaria* (Zhou, Zhang & Fang, 1991) und *Pelodiscus parviformis* Tang, 1997 ist unklar; erstere basiert laut Zhao (1997) vermutlich auf Jungtieren von *Pelodiscus sinensis*, letztere ist nur schwach definiert. Sollten beide Arten sich als eigenständig erweisen, existieren zudem laut Fritz & Obst (1999) mit hoher Wahrscheinlichkeit ältere verfügbare Namen, da die Liste der Synonyme von *Pelodiscus sinensis* sehr lang ist. Aus diesem Grunde werden diese beiden „Arten" bis zum Vorliegen weiterer Untersuchungsergebnisse hier nicht aufgeführt.

How to use this book

Guidelines on the captive husbandry of each species and subspecies are provided in an insert at the end of this book. Please also take note of the following general advice:

A separation of male and female turtles outside the mating season should be striven for in every species. Otherwise, the reproductive success will be considerably reduced, even in peaceful species. Only a few species appear to necessitate a constant joint keeping of the sexes to reproduce successfully. As many keepers cannot afford housing their animals separately or in spacious enclosures, strict separation of sexes (or even the solitary husbandry of individual turtles) is recommended only for species where these precautions are considered to be absolutely necessary to warrant both the well-being of the animals and regular reproductive success.

As far as terrarium dimensions are concerned, I ask the readers to consider them as **minimum requirements**. As this book is mainly (but of course not exclusively) addressed to a German-speaking readership, the recommendations for keeping species in outdoor enclosures always refer to Central European climatic conditions. Finally, the husbandry recommendations given in this book of course do **not** replace the study of special literature about turtle husbandry.

Benutzerhinweise

Richtlinien zur Haltung der abgebildeten Arten und Unterarten sind der ausklappbaren Tafel am Ende des Buches zu entnehmen. Folgende allgemeine Hinweise seien jedoch an dieser Stelle dem Bildteil vorangestellt.

Absolut erstrebenswert ist bei allen Arten eine getrennte Haltung der Geschlechter außerhalb der Paarungszeit; selbst bei verträglichen Schildkrötenarten führt eine nur zeitweise Vergesellschaftung männlicher und weiblicher Tiere meist zu einer deutlichen Steigerung des Nachzuchterfolges. Da aber vielen Schildkrötenhaltern eine getrennte Haltung oder die Unterbringung der Tiere in sehr weitläufigen Anlagen schlichtweg nicht möglich ist, habe ich hier die Empfehlung „Geschlechtertrennung" oder gar „Einzelhaltung" nur für solche Arten übernommen, bei denen ich nach sorgfältigem Abwägen zu dem Ergebnis gekommen bin, dass diese Art der Haltung für die Gesundheit der Tiere oder den regelmäßigen Zuchterfolg absolut notwendig ist.

Was die Angaben zur Behältergröße betrifft, so sind sie als das zu betrachten, als was sie auch bezeichnet wurden, nämlich als **Mindestanforderungen**. Da dieses Buch sich überwiegend (wenn auch nicht ausschließlich) an die deutschsprachige Leserschaft wendet, beziehen sich auch die Empfehlungen zur Freilandhaltung auf mitteleuropäische Verhältnisse. Abschließend sei noch bemerkt, dass die hier aufgeführten Haltungsempfehlungen selbstverständlich **nicht** das Studium weiterführender Literatur zur Pflege der Schildkröten ersetzen können und wollen.

Fig. 1: Turtle vendors, Qing Ping Market, Guangzhou, China / Schildkrötenhändler, Qing-Ping-Markt, Guangzhou, China, May 2000. P.P. van Dijk

Fig. 2: Turtle products in the same market / Schildkrötenprodukte auf demselben Markt. P.P. van Dijk

References/Literaturverzeichnis

The following bibliography exclusively lists references cited in the introduction. The appendix, however, mentions some more general books dealing with the chelonians inhabiting the area dealt with in this volume/*Das folgende Literaturverzeichnis nennt ausschließlich Arbeiten, auf die in der Einführung Bezug genommen wird. Im Anschluss seien jedoch einige allgemeinere Werke genannt, die sich intensiver mit den Schildkröten der in diesem Band behandelten Region befassen.*

ARTNER (2003): Die rezenten Schildkrötenarten der Erde. – Emys, Sitzenberg-Reidling, **10** (6): IV–XXXVIII.

BARTH, BERNHARD, FRITZSCH & FRITZ (2004): The freshwater turtle genus *Mauremys* (Testudines, Geoemydidae) – a textbook example of an east-west disjunction or a taxonomic misconcept? – Zoologica Scripta, Oxford, **33** (3): 213–221.

BARTH, BERNHARD, GUICKING, STOCK & FRITZ (2003): Is *Chinemys megalocephala* FANG, 1934 a valid species? New insights based on mitochondrial DNA sequence data. – Salamandra, Rheinbach, **38** (4): 233–244.

BOUR (1980): Essai sur la taxinomie des Testudinidae actuels (Reptilia, Chelonii). – Bulletin du Muséum National d'Histoire Naturelle, Paris, 4, 2 A (2): 541–546.

BLANCK & TANG (2005): Ein neuer Fundort von *Cuora pani* SONG, 1984 mit Diskussion über den taxonomischen Status von *Cuora pani* und *Cuora aurocapitata*. – Sacalia, Stiefern, **3** (7): 16–37.

BOUR (1985): Les tortues terrestres géantes des îles de locéan Indien Occidental – données géographiques, taxinomiques et phylogénétiques. – *In*: DE BROIN & JIMENEZ-FUENTES (Eds.): Studia Palaeochelonologica, Studia Geologica Salmanticensia, Volumen Especial 1. – Salamanca (Ediciones Universidad de Salamanca): 17–76.

BOUR (2004): *Centrochelys sulcata* (MILLER, 1779) et *Stigmochelys pardalis* (BELL, 1827). – Manouria, Mezzavia, **7** (24): 9–13.

BOUR & DUBOIS (1986): Nomenclature ordinale et familiale des Tortues (Reptilia) – Note complémentaire. – Bulletin Mensuel de la Société Linnéenne de Lyon, Lyon, **55** (3): 87–90.

BOWEN, MEYLAN, ROSS, LIMPUS, BALAZS & AVISE (1992): Global population structure and natural history of the green turtle (*Chelonia mydas*) in terms of matriarchal phylogeny. – Evolution, Lawrence, **46**: 865–881.

CHKHIKVADZE (1987): O sistematicheskom poloshenii dalnevostochnogo Trioniksa. – Bulletin of the Academy of Sciences of the Georgian SSSR, Tiflis, **128** (3): 609–610.

DAS (2001): Die Schildkröten des Indischen Subkontinents. – Frankfurt am Main (Edition Chimaira), 181 pp.

DAVID (1994): Liste des reptiles actuels du monde – I – Chelonii. – Dumerilia, Paris, 1, 128 pp.

DIESMOS, PARHAM, STUART & BROWN (2005): The phylogenetic position of the recently rediscovered Philippine Forest Turtle (Bataguridae: *Heosemys leytensis*). – Proceedings of the California Academy of Sciences, San Francisco, **56** (3): 31–41.

ERNST & LAEMMERZAHL (2002): Geographic variation in the Asian big-headed turtle, *Platysternon megacephalum* (Reptilia: Testudines: Platysternidae). – Proceedings of the Biological Society of Washington, Washington, **115** (1): 18–24.

FARKAS & WEBB (2003): *Rafetus leloii* HÀ DÌNH DÚC, 2000 – an invalid species of softshell turtle from Hoan Kiem Lake, Hanoi, Vietnam (Reptilia, Testudines, Trionychidae). – Zoologische Abhandlungen des Staatlichen Museums für Tierkunde Dresden, Dresden, **53**: 107–112.

FELDMAN & PARHAM (2004): Molecular Systematics of Old World Stripe-Necked Turtles (Testudines: *Mauremys*). – Asiatic Herpetological Research, Berkeley, **10**: 28–37.

FRITZ (2001): Bataguridae – Altweltliche Sumpfschildkröten. – *In*: FRITZ (Ed.): Handbuch der Reptilien und Amphibien Europas, Band 3/IIIA, Schildkröten (Testudines) I. Wiebelsheim (AULA-Verlag): 33–34.

FRITZ & OBST (1996): Zur Kenntnis der Celebes-Erdschildkröte, *Heosemys yuwonoi* (MCCORD, IVERSON & BOEADI, 1995). – herpetofauna, Weinstadt, **18** (102): 27–34.

FRITZ & OBST (1997): Zum taxonomischen Status von *Cuora galbinifrons serrata* IVERSON & MCCORD 1992 und *Pyxidea mouhotii* (GRAY, 1862) (Reptilia: Testudines: Bataguridae). – Zoologische Abhandlungen des Staatlichen Museums für Tierkunde Dresden, Dresden, **49**: 261–279.

FRITZ & OBST (1999): Neue Schildkröten aus Südostasien – Teil II – Bataguridae (*Cyclemys, Heosemys, Mauremys, Ocadia, Pyxidea, Sacalia*) und Trionychidae. – Sauria, Berlin, **21** (1): 11–26.

GAFFNEY & MEYLAN (1988): A phylogeny of turtles. *In*: BENTON (Ed.): The Phylogeny and Classification of the Tetrapods – Volume 1 – Amphibia, Reptilia, Birds – Systematics Association, Special Volume 35 A. – Oxford (Clarendon Press): 157–219.

GERLACH (2001): Tortoise phylogeny and the *Geochelone* problem. – Phelsuma, Victoria, **9** (A): 1–23.

GUICKING, FRITZ, WINK & LEHR (2002): New data on the diversity of the Southeast Asian leaf turtle genus *Cyclemys* BELL, 1834 – Molecular results (Reptilia: Testudines: Geoemydidae). – Faunistische Abhandlungen des Staatlichen Museums für Tierkunde Dresden, Dresden, **23**: 76–86.

GUO, NIE & WANG (1997): The karyotypes and NORs of two species of *Chinemys*. – Sichuan Journal of Zoology, Volume 15 (Supplement), Herpetological Series 9, Chinese Chelonian Research: 97–103.

HÀ DÌNH DÚC (2000): Rua Ho Guom Loai Rua Moicho Khoa Hoc. – Khao co Hoc, Hanoi, **4**: 104–111.

HONDA, YASUKAWA & OTA (2002): Phylogeny of the Eurasian freshwater turtles of the genus *Mauremys* GRAY, 1869 (Testudinidae), with special reference to a close affinity of *Mauremys japonica* with *Chinemys reevesii*. – Journal of Zoological Systematic and Evolution Research, Oxford, **40**: 195–200.

ICZN (1999): International Code of Zoological Nomenclature – 4. edition. – London (International Trust for Zoological Nomenclature), XXIX + 306 pp.

IVERSON (1992): A Revised Checklist with Distribution Maps of the Turtles of the World. – Richmond (privately printed), 363 pp.

IVERSON & MCCORD (1992a): A new Chinese eyed turtle of the genus *Sacalia* (Batagurinae: Testudines). – Proceedings of the Biological Society of Washington, Washington, **105** (3): 426–432.

IVERSON & MCCORD (1992b): A new subspecies of *Cuora galbinifrons* (Testudines: Batagurinae) from Hainan island, China. – Proceedings of the Biological Society of Washington, Washington, **105** (3): 433–439.

IVERSON, ERNST, GOTTE & LOVICH (1989): The validity of *Chinemys megalocephala* (Testudines: Batagurinae). – Copeia, Lawrence, 2: 494–498.

IVERSON, SPINKS, SHAFFER, MCCORD & DAS (2001): Phylogenetic relationships among the Asian tortoises of the genus

Indotestudo (Reptilia: Testudines: Testudinidae). – Hamadryad, Mamallapuram, **26** (2): 272–275.

KARL & BOWEN (1999): Evolutionary significant units versus geopolitical taxonomy – molecular systematics of an endangered sea turtle (genus *Chelonia*). – Conservation Biology, Arlington, **13** (5): 990–999.

MCCORD (1997): *Mauremys pritchardi*, a new batagurid turtle from Myanmar and Yunnan, China. – Chelonian Conservation and Biology, Lunenburg, **2** (4): 555–562.

MCCORD & IVERSON (1992): A new species of *Ocadia* (Testudines: Bataguridae) from Hainan Island, China. – Proceedings of the Biological Society of Washington, Washington, **105** (1): 13–18.

MCCORD & IVERSON (1994): A new species of *Ocadia* (Testudines: Batagurinae) from southwestern China. – Proceedings of the Biological Society of Washington, Washington, **107** (1): 52–59.

MCCORD & JOSEPH-OUNI (2004): Chelonian Illustrations #16. Pond, Thread, and Four-Eyed Turtles of Eastern Asia. – Reptilia (GB), Barcelona, 36: 10–13.

MCCORD, IVERSON & BOEADI (1995): A new batagurid turtle from northern Sulawesi, Indonesia. – Chelonian Conservation and Biology, Lunenburg, **1** (4): 311–316.

MCCORD, IVERSON, SPINKS & SHAFFER (2000): A new genus of geoemydid turtle from Asia. – Hamadryad, Mamallapuram, **25** (2): 86–90.

MOLL (1985): Relationship and biology of the chelonian genus *Kachuga* in India. – Annual Meetings Society for the Study of Amphibians and Reptiles/Herpetologists League, University of South Florida, Tampa.

MOLL (1986): Survey of the freshwater turtles of India – Part I – The genus *Kachuga*. – Journal of the Bombay Natural History Society, Bombay, **83**: 538–552.

MOLL (1987): Survey of the freshwater turtles of India – Part II – The genus *Kachuga*. – Journal of the Bombay Natural History Society, Bombay, **84**: 7–25.

PARHAM, SIMSON, KOZAK, FELDMAN & SHI (2001): New Chinese turtles – endangered or invalid? A reassessment of two species using mitochondrial DNA, allozyme electrophoresis and known locality specimens. – Animal Conservation, London, 4: 357–367.

PHILIPPEN (2004): Bedrohte Landschildkröten. – Marginata, Münster, **1** (3): 9–12.

PRASCHAG, SCHMIDT, FRITZSCH, MÜLLER, GEMEL & FRITZ (2006): *Geoemyda silvatica*, an enigmatic turtle of the Geoemydidae (Reptilia: Testudines), represents a distinct genus. – Organisms Diversity & Evolution, **6**: 151–162.

PRITCHARD (2000): *Indotestudo travancorica*… a Valid Species of Tortoise? – Reptile & Amphibian Hobbyist, Neptune City, **5** (6): 18–28.

PRITCHARD & MCCORD (1991): A new emydid turtle from China. – Herpetologica, Emporia, **47** (2): 139–147.

SCHLEICH & KÄSTLE (Eds.) (2002): Amphibians and Reptiles of Nepal. – Ruggell (A. R. G. Gantner Verlag), 1201 pp.

SPINKS, SHAFFER, IVERSON & MCCORD (2004): Phylogenetic hypotheses for the turtle family Geoemydidae. – Molecular Phylogenetics and Evolution, **32** (1): 164–182.

STUART & PARHAM (2004): Molecular phylogeny of the critically endangered Indochinese box turtle (*Cuora galbinifrons*). – Molecular Phylogenetics and Evolution, **31** (1): 164–177.

TANG (1997): Research on a new species of *Pelodiscus*, Trionychidae, in China. – Zoological Research, Kunming, **18** (1): 13–17.

WEBB (1995): Redescription and neotype designation of *Pelochelys bibroni* from southern New Guinea (Testudines: Trionychidae). – Chelonian Conservation and Biology, Lunenburg, **1** (4): 301–310.

WINK, GUICKING & FRITZ (2001): Molecular evidence for hybrid origin of *Mauremys iversoni* PRITCHARD et MCCORD, 1991, and *Mauremys pritchardi* MCCORD, 1997 (Reptilia: Testudines: Bataguridae). – Zoologische Abhandlungen des Staatlichen Museums für Tierkunde Dresden, **51** (5): 41–49.

YASUKAWA, OTA & HIKADA (1992): Taxonomic re-evaluation of the two subspecies of *Geoemyda spengleri spengleri* (GMELIN, 1789) (Reptilia: Emydidae). – Japanese Journal of Herpetology, Kyoto, **14** (3): 143–159.

ZHAO (1997): Studies on the classification of Chinese soft-shelled turtles (Trionychidae). – *In*: ZHAO (Ed.): Chinese Chelonian Research. – Chinese Society for the Study of Amphibians and Reptiles, Herpetological Series No. 9, Sichuan Journal of Zoology, 15 (Supplement): 55–64.

ZHOU, ZHANG & FANG (1991): Bulletin of a new species *Trionyx*. – Acta Sci. Nat. Univ. Norm., Hunan Changsha, **14** (4): 379–382.

General sources/Allgemeine Literatur

Asia in general/Asien allgemein

ARTNER, FARKAS & LOEHR (Eds.) (2006): Turtles. Proceedings: International Turtle & Tortoise Symposium Vienna 2002.– Frankfurt am Main (Edition Chimaira): 618 pp.

DAS (1996): Biogeography of the Reptiles of South Asia. – Malabar (Krieger Publishing Company), 87 pp.

DAS (2002): An Introduction to the Amphibians and Reptiles of Tropical Asia. – Kota Kinabalu (Natural History Publications [Borneo]), 207 pp.

MOLL & MOLL (2004): The Ecology, Exploitation and Conservation of River Turtles. – Oxford & New York (Oxford University Press), 393 pp.

VAN DIJK, STUART & RHODIN (Eds.) (2000): Asian Turtle Trade: Proceedings of a Workshop on Conservation and Trade of Freshwater Turtles and Tortoises in Asia. – Chelonian Research Monographs No. 2, Lunenburg (Chelonian Research Foundation), 164 pp.

SCHILDE (2004): Asiatische Sumpfschildkröten. Die Familie Geoemydidae in Südostasien, China und Japan. – Münster (Natur und Tier - Verlag), 190 pp.

China & Taiwan

DE BRUIN & ARTNER (1999): On the turtles of Hainan Island, southern China. – Chelonian Conservation and Biology, Lunenburg, **3** (3): 479–486.

KARSEN, LAU & BOGADEK (1998): Hong Kong Amphibians and Reptiles – 2nd Edition. – Hong Kong (Provisional Urban Council), 186 pp.

LUE, TU & SHANG (1999): Field Guide of Amphibians and Reptiles in Taiwan. – Taipei (Society for Wildlife and Nature), 343 pp.

MAO (1971): Turtles of Taiwan. – Taipei (The Commercial Press), 128 pp.

POPE (1935): Natural History of Central Asia, Vol. X: The Reptiles of China. – New York (The American Museum of Natural History), 548 pp.

WANG (Ed.) (1998): China Red Data Book of Endangered Animals. Amphibia & Reptilia. – Beijing, Hong Kong & New York (Science Press), 330 pp. + IV color plates.

YE (1994): Fossil and Recent Turtles of China. – Beijing (Science Press), 112 pp. + 1 color plate.

ZHANG, ZONG & MA (1998): Fauna Sinica, Reptilia Vol. I. – Beijing (Science Press), 214 pp. + IV color plates.

ZHAO (Ed.) (1997): Chinese Chelonian Research. – Chinese Society for the Study of Amphibians and Reptiles, Herpetological Series No. 9, Sichuan Journal of Zoology, 15 (Supplement), 159 pp.

ZHAO (1998): China Red Data Book of Endangered Animals. Vol. 3. Amphibia and Reptilia. – Beijing (Science Press), 330 pp.

ZHAO & ADLER (1993): Herpetology of China. – Oxford (Society for the Study of Amphibians and Reptiles), Contributions in Herpetology No. 10, 522 pp.

ZHOU & ZHOU (1992): Chinese Chelonians Illustrated. – Jiangsu Science and Technology Publishing House (Nanjing), 89 pp.

Indian Subcontinent/Indischer Subkontinent

DAS (1985): Indian Turtles: A Field Guide. – Calcutta (World Wildlife Fund-India, Eastern Region), 119 pp.

DAS (1991): Colour Guide to the Turtles and Tortoises of the Indian Subcontinent. – Portishead (R & A Publishing), 133 pp.

DAS (1995): Turtles and Tortoises of India. – Bombay, Delhi, Calcutta & Madras (Oxford University Press), 179 pp.

DAS (2001): Die Schildkröten des Indischen Subkontinents. – Frankfurt am Main (Edition Chimaira), 181 pp.

DERANIYAGALA (1939): The Tetrapod Reptiles of Ceylon. Vol. I. Testudinates and Crocodilians. – Colombo (Colombo Museum), 412 pp.

GARDINER (Ed.) (1903): The Fauna and Geography of the Maldive and Laccadive Archipelagoes, being the account of the work carried out and collections made by an expedition during the years 1899 and 1900. Vol. I. – Cambridge (University Press).

KHAN (1982): Chelonians of Bangladesh and their Conservation. – Journal of the Bombay Natural History Society, Bombay, **79** (1): 110–116.

KHAN (1987): Bangladesher Bannya Prani. Vol. 1 (Amphibians and Reptiles). – Dhaka (Bangla Academy), 168 pp.

KHAN (2006): Amphibians and Reptiles of Pakistan. – Malabar (Krieger Publishing), 328 pp.

KHAN & MIRZA (1976): An Annotated Checklist and Key to the Reptiles of Pakistan. Part I: Chelonia and Crocodilia. – Biologica, Lahore, **22**: 211–220.

SCHLEICH & KÄSTLE (Eds.) (2002): Amphibians and Reptiles of Nepal. – Ruggell (A. R. G. Gantner Verlag), 1201 pp.

SHARMA (1998): The Fauna of India and Adjacent Countries. Reptilia Volume I (Testudines and Crocodilia). – Calcutta (Zoological Survey of India), 196 pp.

SHRESTHA (2001): Herpetology of Nepal. – Kathmandu (privately printed), 280 pp.

SMITH (1931): The Fauna of British India, including Ceylon and Burma – Reptilia and Amphibia. Vol. 1. – Loricata, Testudines. London (Taylor & Francis Ltd. for the India Office), xxviii +185 pp.

TIKADER & SHARMA (1985): Handbook Indian Testudines. – Calcutta (Zoological Survey of India), 155 pp.

VENKATAMARAN & MILTON (2003): Marine Turtles of India. – Kolkata (Zoological Survey of India), 87 pp.

Japan

GORIS & MAEDA (2005): Guide to the Amphibians and Reptiles of Japan. – Malabar (Krieger Publishing Company), 283 pp.

MATSUI & OTA (1999): Amphibians and Reptiles. – *In*: Endangered Wildlife of Japan, Red Data Book 2nd ed. – Tokyo (Japan Agency of Environment).

Russia/Russland

KUZMIN (2002): The Turtles of Russia and Other Ex-Soviet Republics. – Frankfurt am Main (Edition Chimaira), 159 pp

SZCZERBAK (2003): Guide to the Reptiles of the Eastern Palearctic. – Malabar (Krieger Publishing Company), 260 pp.

Southeast Asia/Südostasien

BOURRET (1941): Les Tortues de l'Indochine – Notes de l'Institut Océanographique de l'Indochine, Hanoi, 38, 235 pp. (reprint by/Nachdruck durch *Society for the Study of Amphibians and Reptiles* 2005).

CHAN-ARD, GROSSMANN, GUMPRECHT & SCHULZ (1999): Amphibians and Reptiles of Peninsular Malaysia and Thailand. – Würselen (Bushmaster Publications), 240 pp.

COX, VAN DIJK, NABHITABHATA & THIRAKHUPT (1998): A Photographic guide to snakes and Other Reptiles of Peninsular Malaysia, Singapore and Thailand. – London, Cape Town, Sydney & Singapore (New Holland Publishers), 144 pp.

DE ROOIJ (1915): The Reptiles of the Indo-Australian Archipelago. Vol. I. Lacertilia, Chelonia, Emydosauria. – Leiden (E. J. Brill), 384 pp.

JENKINS (1995): Tortoises and Freshwater Turtles: The Trade in Southeast Asia. – Cambridge (TRAFFIC International), IV + 48 pp.

LIM & DAS (1999): Turtles of Borneo and Peninsular Malaysia. – Kota Kinabalu (Natural History Publications [Borneo]), 151 pp.

LIM & LIM (1992): A Guide to the amphibians and Reptiles of Singapore. – Singapore (Singapore Science Centre), 160 p.

MANTHEY & GROSSMANN (1997): Amphibien & Reptilien Südostasiens. – Münster (Natur und Tier – Verlag), 512 pp.

NUTAPHAND (1979): The Turtles of Thailand. – Bangkok (Siam Farm Zoological Gardens), 222 pp.

SMITH (1931): The Fauna of British India, including Ceylon and Burma – Reptilia and Amphibia. Vol. 1. – Loricata, Testudines. London (Taylor & Francis Ltd. for the India Office), xxviii +185 pp.

STUART, VAN DIJK & HENDRIE (2001): Photographic Guide to the Turtles of Thailand, Laos, Vietnam and Cambodia. – New York (Wildlife conservation Society), 84 pp.

TAYLOR (1920): Philippine Turtles. – Philippine J. Sci., **16**: 111–144.

TAYLOR (1970): The turtles and Crocodiles of Thailand and Adjacent Waters. – The University of Kansas Science Bulletin, Lawrence, **XLIX** (3): 87-179.

WIN MAUNG & WIN KO KO (2002): Turtles & tortoises of Myanmar. – Yangon (Wildife Conservation Society), 94 pp.

Acknowledgments/Danksagung

Pictures taken in the wild were principally preferred when selecting the material for this volume. Only in a few cases captive animals are shown.
For providing us with their pictures we are grateful to the following persons/
Bei der Auswahl der Bilder wurde Aufnahmen im natürlichen Lebensraum der Vorzug gegeben. In Einzelfällen musste auf Fotos von Tieren in menschlicher Obhut zurückgegriffen werden.
Den folgenden Personen möchten wir hiermit für die freundliche Bereitstellung ihres Bildmaterials herzlich danken:

Eduard V. Adnagulov, Khabarovsk/Russia; Rémy Amann, Guebwiller/France; Harald Artner, Sitzenberg-Reidling/Austria; Mark Auliya, Bonn/Germany; Ian Bell, Townsville, QLD/Australia; Thomas Berndt, Zaisenhausen, Germany; Torsten Blanck, Deutschlandsberg/Austria; Olivier Born, Lausanne/Switzerland; Timothy R. Brophy, Lynchburg, VA/USA; Shekar Dattatri, Delhi/India; Indraneil Das, Kota Samarang/Malaysia; E.A. Dunaev, Moscow/Russia; David Emmett, Phnom Penh/Cambodia; Bastian Esser, Aachen/Germany; Pierre Fidenci, San Francisco, CA/USA; Michael Franzen, München/Germany; Frank Galgon, Berlin/Germany; Richard Gemel, Vienna/Austria; Cris Hagen/Aiken, SC/USA; James H. Harding, East Lansing, MI/USA; David Hegner, Jablonec/Czech Rep.; Friedrich Wilhelm Henkel, Kamen/Germany; Andreas S. Hennig, Leipzig/Germany; Doug Hendrie, Hanoi/Viet Nam; Katharina & Wolfgang Heuberger, Aldersbach/Germany; Tsutomu Honda, Tokyo/Japan; Brian D. Horne, Athens, OH/USA; Hu Zewei, Beijing, China; Franz Hummel, Vienna/Austria; Herda Hutabarat, Zandvoort, The Netherlands; John B. Iverson, Richmond, IN/USA; Urs Jost, St. Erhard/Switzerland; Nobuhiro Kawazoe; Creeper, Tokyo/Japan; Michael Koch, Mainz/Gemany; André Koch, Bonn/Gemany; Kai Olaf Krüger, Angkor/Cambodia; Gerald Kuchling, Perth/Australia; Lin Ying, Shanghai/China; Matthias Mähn, Winnweiler/Germany; Jérôme Maran, Ayguesvives/France; William P. McCord, Hopewell Junction, NY/USA; Andreas Mende, Zaisenhausen/Germany; Mian Hou, Chengdu/China; Michael Nesbit, Bloomington, IL/USA; Edward O. Moll, Tucson, AZ/USA; Shomen Mukherjee, Mumbai/India; Andreas Nöllert, Jena/Germany; Ben Osborne, Bristol/UK; James F. Parham, San Francisco, CA/USA; Sascha Pawlowski, Lampertheim/Germany; Remix Peponi, Tokyo/Japan; Petr Petras, Pardubice/Czech Rep.; Hans-Dieter Philippen, Heinsberg/Germany; Peter Praschag, Graz/Austria; Reiner Praschag, Graz/Austria; Hynek Prokop, Pardubice/Czech Rep.; Oliver Römpp, Dewangen/Germany; Manfred Rogner, Hürtgenwald/Germany; Walter Sachsse, Mainz/Germany; Maik Schilde, Leipzig/Germany; Gerhard Schaffer, Stiefern/Austria; Christian Schneiter, Boll/Switzerland; Patrick Schönecker, Berschweiler/Germany; Stefan Seebacher, Aigen/Austria; Shintaro Seki, Shigaken/Japan; Ruchira Somaweera, Kandy/Sri Lanka; Karl H. Switak, Santa Rosa, CA/USA; Steffen Szymanski, Kronau/Germany; Michael Tang, Hong Kong/China; Ting Zhou, Nanjing/China; Ulrich Thieme, Potsdam/Germany; John Thorbjarnarson, Gainesville, FL/USA; Dietmar Trobisch, Bilkheim/Germany; Jaroslav Vogeltanz, Plzen/Czech Rep.; Bernd Wolff, Lingenfeld/Germany; Fritz Wüthrich, Wimmis/Switzerland; Thomas Ziegler, Köln/Germany; Zu-yi Zhou, Cheng-du/China; Henk Zwartepoorte, Rotterdam/The Netherlands.

The three of us would not have been able to gather this collection of photos without the help of the following friends and colleagues. We would like to express our gratitude for their support in particular to/
Ohne die engagierte Hilfe der folgenden Freunde und Kollegen wäre es nicht möglich gewesen, die Abbildungen für den vorliegenden Band zusammenzustellen. Herzlich danken wir:

Kraig Adler, Ithaca NY/USA; Harry Andrews, Mamallapuram/India; Yukio Asaoka, Yokohama/Japan; Mark Auliya, Bonn/Germany; Dhruvayothi Basu, Kukrail/India; Paul Crow, Hong Kong; Balázs Farkas, Budapest/Hungary; Hubert Felsner, Langenlois/Austria; Frank Glaw, München/Germany; Doug Hendrie, Hanoi/Viet Nam; Andreas Hofer, Krenglbach/Austria; Ludek Hojny, Nove Mesto nad Metuji/Czech Rep.; Kittipong Jarutanin, Bangkok/Thailand; Raymond Kan, Hong Kong; Wachira Kitimasak, Bangkok/Thailand; Sergei L. Kuzmin, Moscow/Russia; Michael Lau Wai Neng, Hong Kong; Anders Lindstrøm, Pattaya/Thailand; Elmar Meier, Münster/Germany; Jonathan Murrray, Bangkok/Thailand; Hans-Dieter Philippen, Heinsberg/Germany; R.J. Rao, Gwalior/India; Dionysius S.K. Sharma, Petaling Jaya/Malaysia; Hiroki Shibata, Fukuoka/Japan; Kumthorn Thirakhupt, Bangkok/Thailand; Thomas Ulber, Bredell/South Africa; Romulus Whitaker, Mamallapuram/India; Fritz Wüthrich, Wimmis/Switzerland.

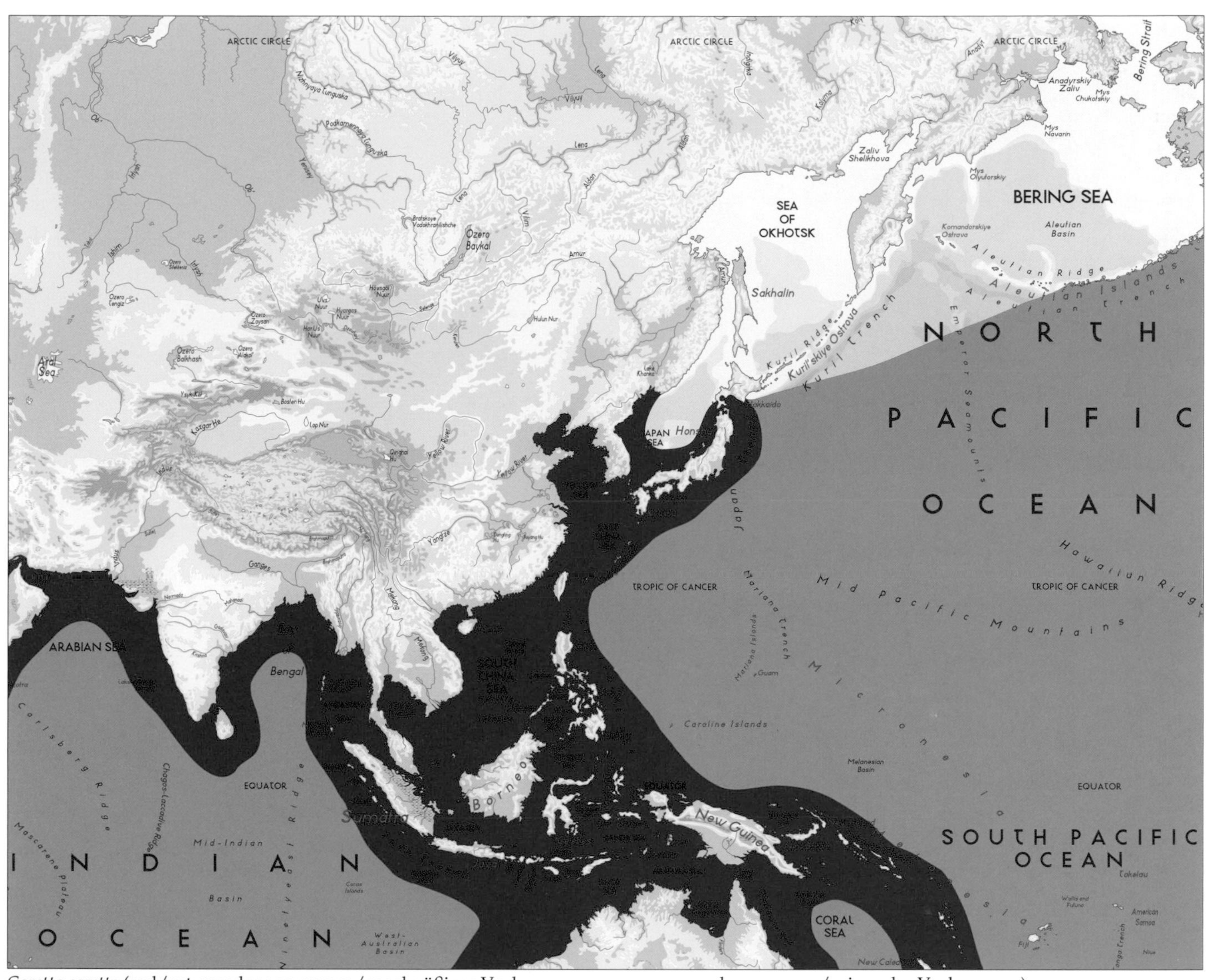

Caretta caretta (red / rot: regular occurrence / regelmäßiges Vorkommen; orange: seasonal occurrence / saisonales Vorkommen)

RT00188-4 *Caretta caretta* (Linnaeus, 1758)
Sri Lanka
135–213 (?) cm

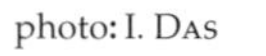
photo: I. Das

RT00189-4 *Caretta caretta* (Linnaeus, 1758)
Sea Turtle Center, Bentota, Sri Lanka
135–213 (?) cm

photo: P.P. van Dijk

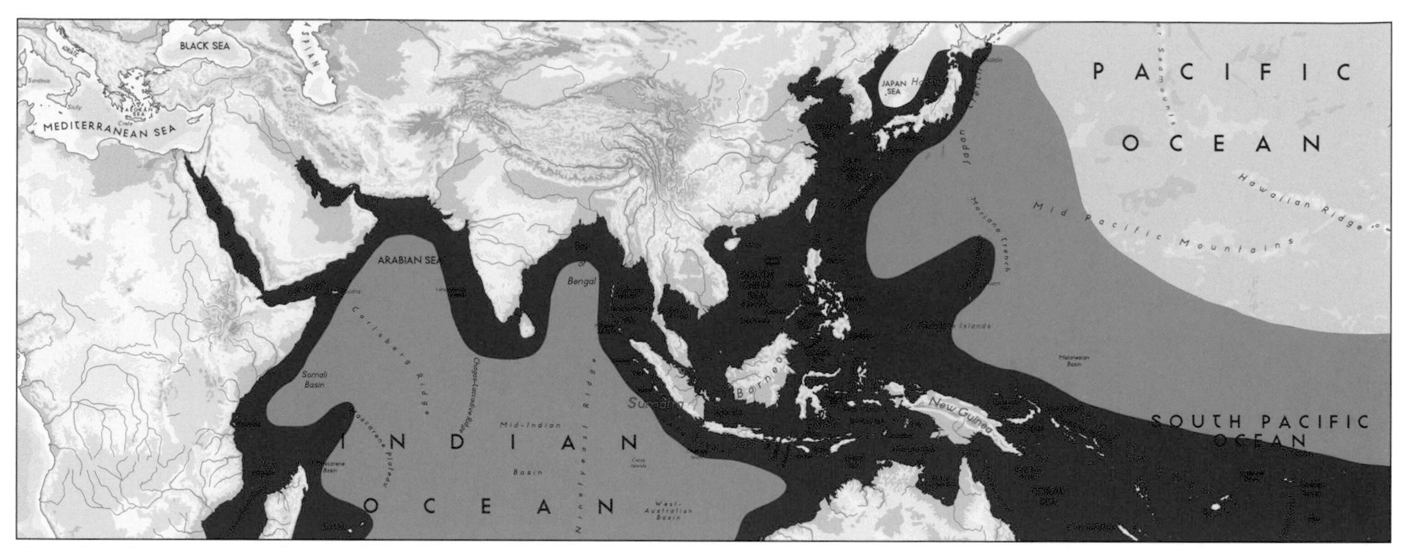

Chelonia mydas japonica (red / rot: regular occurrence / regelmäßiges Vorkommen; orange: seasonal occurrence / saisonales Vorkommen)

RT03991-4 *Chelonia mydas japonica* (THUNBERG, 1787)
140–153 cm
photo: A. NÖLLERT

RT03992-1 *Chelonia mydas japonica* (THUNBERG, 1787)
Sri Lanka
140–153 cm
Opened nest cavity / geöffnete Nistgrube photo: A.S. HENNIG

RT03993-1 *Chelonia mydas japonica* (THUNBERG, 1787)
140–153 cm
Hatchlings / Schlüpflinge photo: P.P. VAN DIJK

RT03994-1 *Chelonia mydas japonica* (THUNBERG, 1787)
Sattahip Turtle Centre, Chonburi, Thailand
140–153 cm
Hatchling / Schlüpfling photo: P.P. VAN DIJK

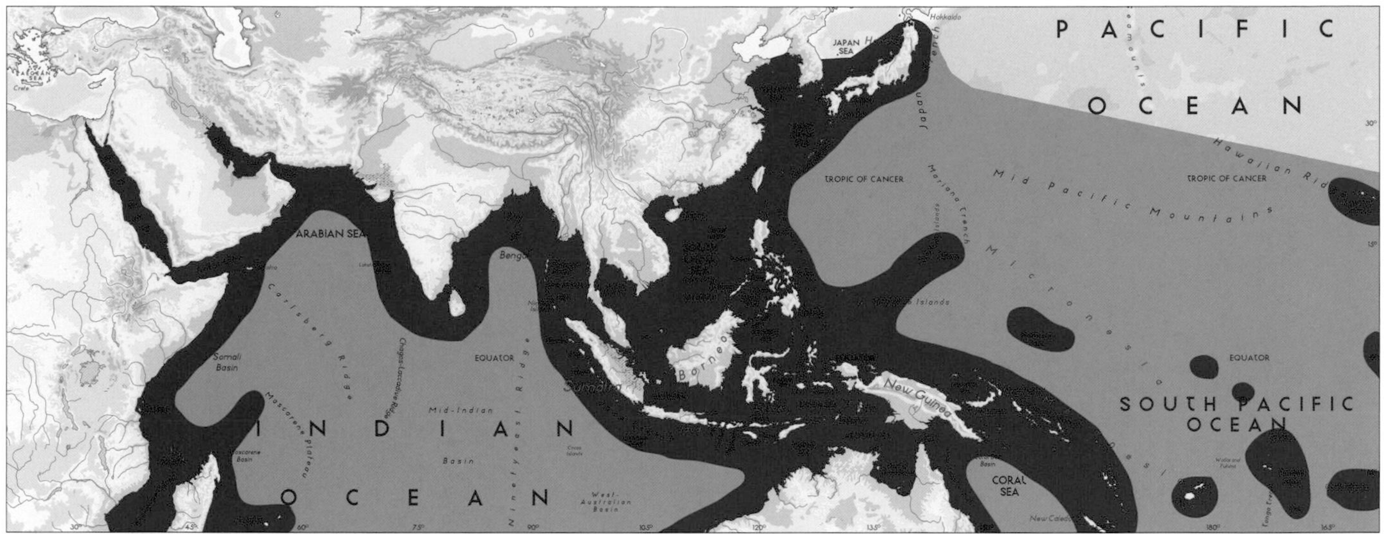

Eretmochelys imbricata bissa (red / rot: regular occurrence / regelmäßiges Vorkommen; orange: seasonal occurrence / saisonales Vorkommen)

RT00054-4 *Eretmochelys imbricata bissa* (RÜPPELL, 1835)

100–114 cm

photo: A. NÖLLERT

RT00055-4 *Eretmochelys imbricata bissa* (RÜPPELL, 1835)
Bentota, Sri Lanka
100–114 cm

photo: S. PAWLOWSKI

RT00056-4 *Eretmochelys imbricata bissa* (RÜPPELL, 1835)
China
100–114 cm

photo: T. BLANCK

RT00057-1 *Eretmochelys imbricata bissa* (RÜPPELL, 1835)
Sattahip Turtle Centre, Chonburi, Thailand
100–114 cm
Hatchling / Schlüpfling

photo: P.P. VAN DIJK

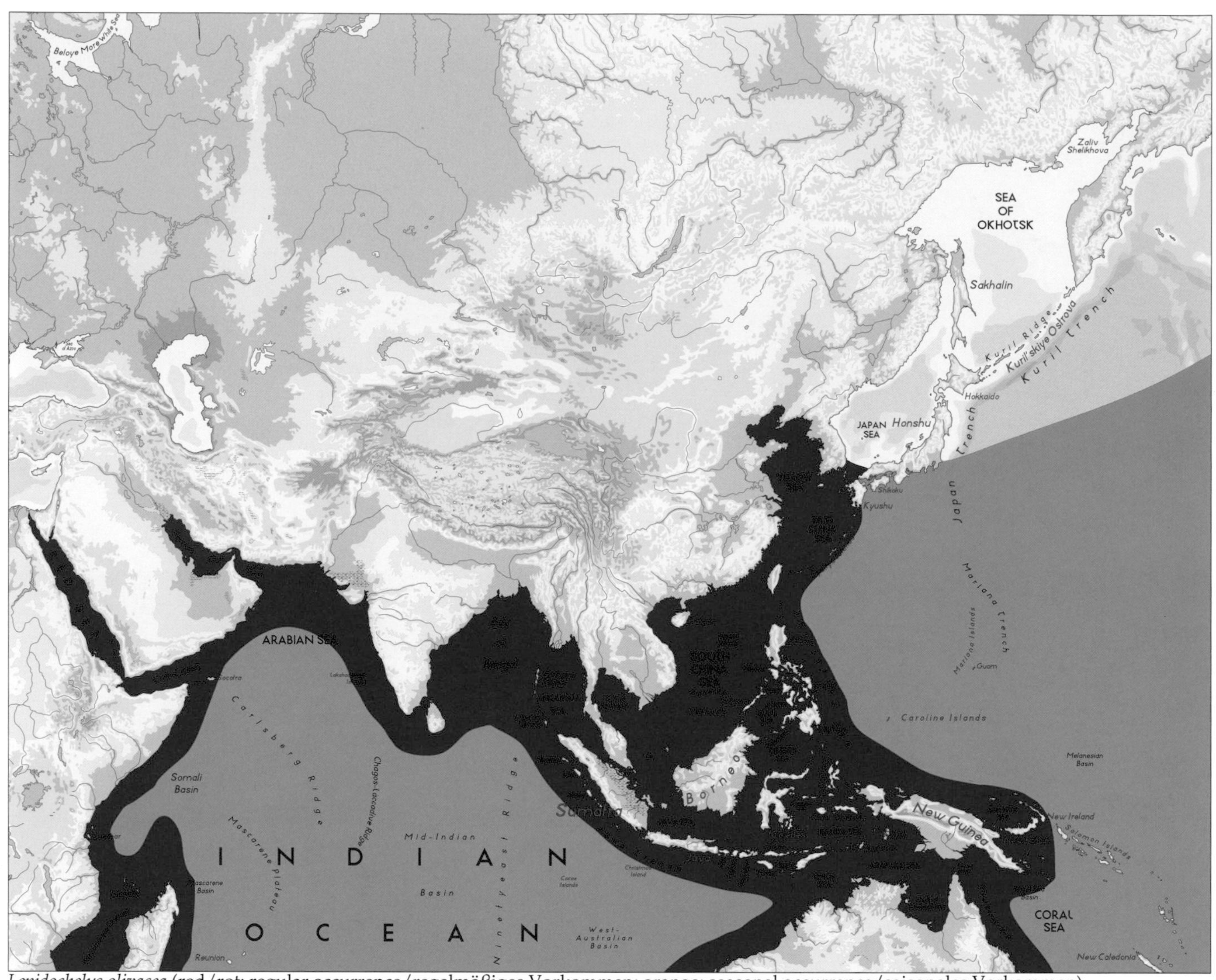

Lepidochelys olivacea (red / rot: regular occurrence / regelmäßiges Vorkommen; orange: seasonal occurrence / saisonales Vorkommen)

RT00065-4 *Lepidochelys olivacea* (Eschscholtz, 1829)
Sattahip Turtle Center, Chonburi, Thailand
70–80 cm

photo: P.P. van Dijk

RT00066-4 *Lepidochelys olivacea* (Eschscholtz, 1829)
Bentota, Sri Lanka
70–80 cm

photo: S. Pawlowski

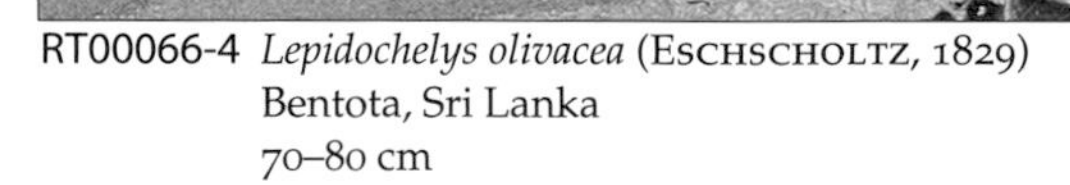

RT00067-4 *Lepidochelys olivacea* (ESCHSCHOLTZ, 1829)
Bentota, Sri Lanka
70–80 cm
Oviposition/Eiablage
photo: S. PAWLOWSKI

RT00068 *Lepidochelys olivacea* (ESCHSCHOLTZ, 1829)
Nesting site, Bentota, Sri Lanka/
Niststrand, Bentota, Sri Lanka
70–80 cm
photo: P.P. VAN DIJK

RT00069-1 *Lepidochelys olivacea* (ESCHSCHOLTZ, 1829)
Weligama, S Sri Lanka
70–80 cm
Hatchling/Schlüpfling
photo: D. HEGNER

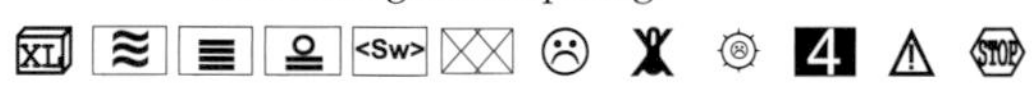

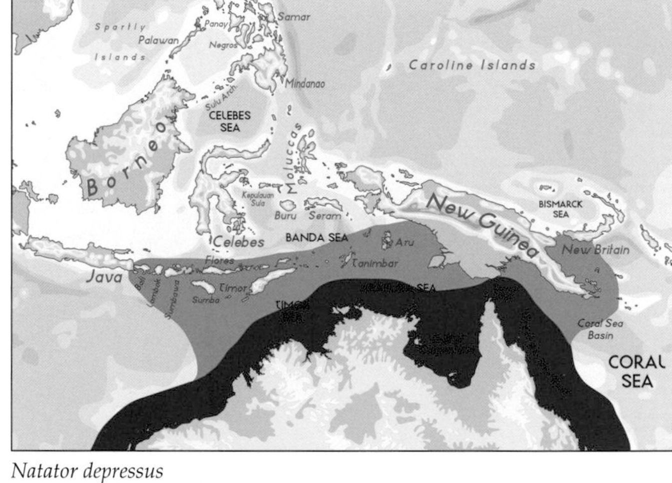

Natator depressus
(red/rot: regular occurrence/regelmäßiges Vorkommen;
orange: seasonal occurrence/saisonales Vorkommen)

RT04001-4 *Natator depressus* (GARMAN, 1880)

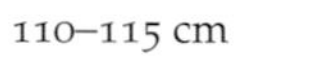
110–115 cm

photo: B. OSBORNE/NATURE PL

RT04002-4 *Natator depressus* (GARMAN, 1880)

110–115 cm

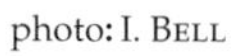
photo: I. BELL

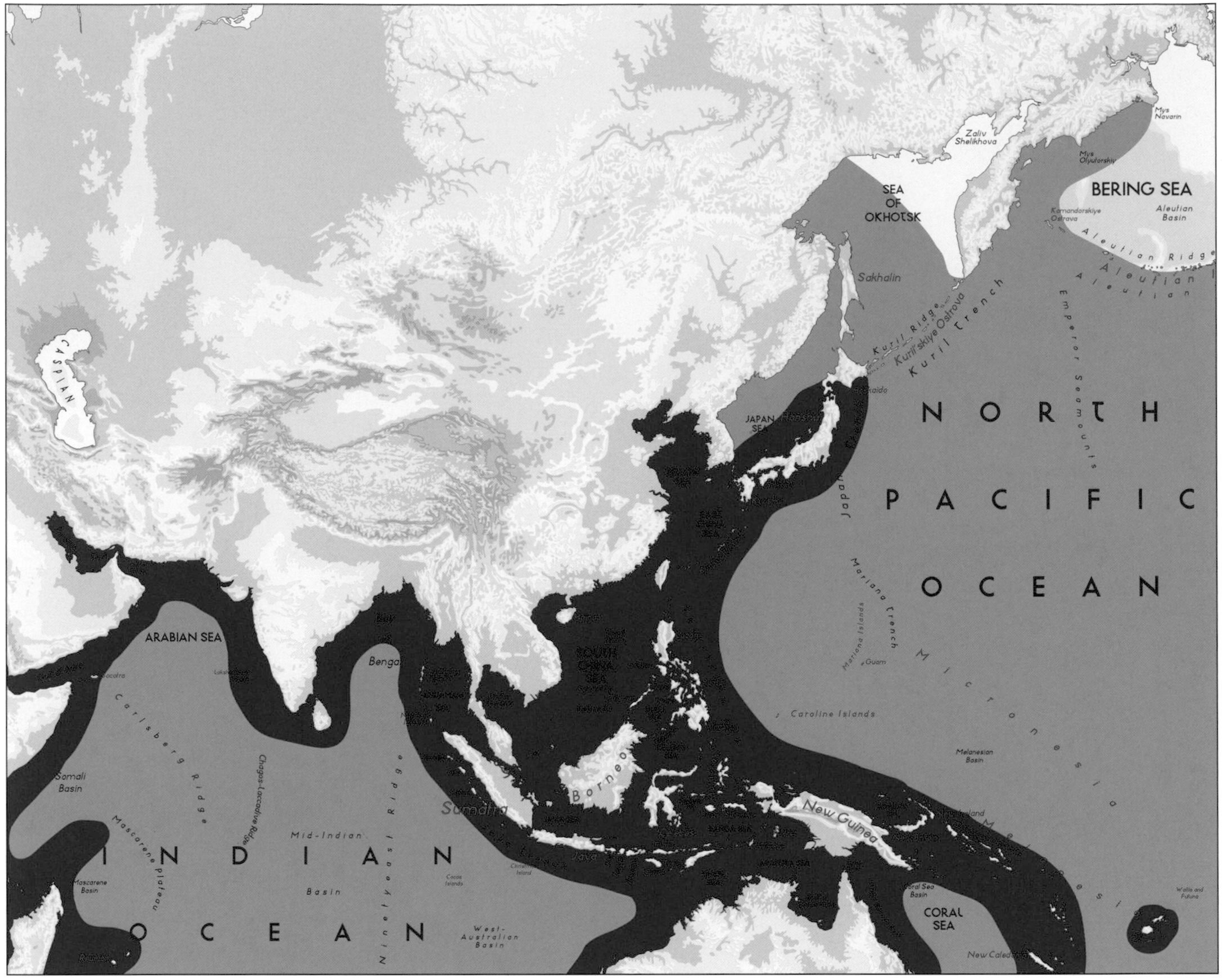

Dermochelys coriacea (red/ro: regular occurrence/regelmäßiges Vorkommen; orange: seasonal occurrence/saisonales Vorkommen)

RT00074-4 *Dermochelys coriacea* (VANDELLI, 1761)
Alas Purwo NP, Banyuwangi, E Java, Indonesia/Indonesien
200–220 cm
photo: H. HUTABARAT

RT00078-2 *Dermochelys coriacea* (VANDELLI, 1761)
Haad Thai Munang, Phang Nga, Thailand
200–220 cm
Juvenile/Jungtier
photo: P.P. VAN DIJK

RT04011-4 *Batagur baska* (Gray, 1831)
Klong La-Ngu, Satun, Thailand
50–65 cm
♀
photo: P.P. van Dijk

RT04012-4 *Batagur baska* (Gray, 1831)

50–65 cm
photo: I. Das

RT04013-1 *Batagur baska* (Gray, 1831)
Klong La-Ngu, Satun, Thailand
50–65 cm
Hatchling/Schlüpfling
photo: P.P. van Dijk

RT04014-2 *Batagur baska* (Gray, 1831)

50–65 cm
Juvenile/Jungtier
photo: J.H. Harding

RT04015 *Batagur baska* (Gray, 1831)
Nesting site/Niststrand, Klong La-Ngu, Satun, Thailand
photo: P.P. van Dijk

Batagur baska (red/rot;
?: questionable occurrence/Vorkommen fraglich;
†: presumably extinct/vermutlich ausgestorben)

RT04021-4 *Callagur borneoensis* (Schlegel & Müller, 1844)
Kuala Setiu, Terengganu, Malaysia
39–76 cm
♀
photo: P.P. van Dijk

RT04022-4 *Callagur borneoensis* (Schlegel & Müller, 1844)
39–76 cm
♂
photo: H. Artner

RT04023-4 *Callagur borneoensis* (Schlegel & Müller, 1844)
Klong La-Ngu, Satun, Thailand
39–76 cm
♀
photo: P.P. van Dijk

RT04024-4 *Callagur borneoensis* (Schlegel & Müller, 1844)
39–76 cm
♂
photo: J. Maran

RT04025-4 *Callagur borneoensis* (Schlegel & Müller, 1844)
Klong La-Ngu, Satun, Thailand
39–76 cm
♀
photo: P.P. van Dijk

RT04026-4 *Callagur borneoensis* (Schlegel & Müller, 1844)
39–76 cm
♂
photo: J. Maran

RT04027-4 *Callagur borneoensis* (Schlegel & Müller, 1844)
Klong La-Ngu, Satun, Thailand
39–76 cm
♀ + ♂
photo: P.P. van Dijk

RT04028-4 *Callagur borneoensis* (Schlegel & Müller, 1844)
Klong La-Ngu, Satun, Thailand
39–76 cm
♂
photo: P.P. van Dijk

RT04029-2 *Callagur borneoensis* (Schlegel & Müller, 1844)

39–76 cm
Juvenile/Jungtier
photo: J.H. Harding

RT04020-4 *Callagur borneoensis* (Schlegel & Müller, 1844)
Klong La-Ngu, Satun, Thailand
39–76 cm
Juvenile/Jungtier
photo: P.P. van Dijk

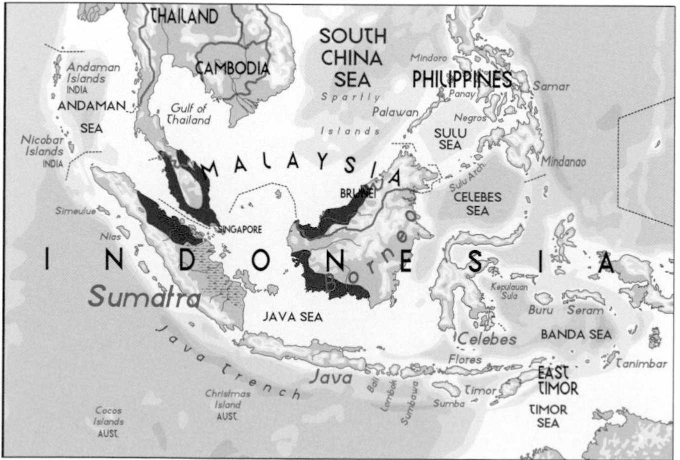

Callagur borneoensis (red/rot)

RT0402X-4 *Callagur borneoensis* (Schlegel & Müller, 1844)
Kuala Setiu, Terengganu, Malaysia
39–76 cm
♀
photo: P.P. van Dijk

RT04031-4 *Cathaiemys annamensis* (SIEBENROCK, 1903)

17–29 cm

photo: J. MARAN

RT04032-4 *Cathaiemys annamensis* (SIEBENROCK, 1903)

17–29 cm
♂ + ♀

photo: U. JOST

RT04033-4 *Cathaiemys annamensis* (SIEBENROCK, 1903)

17–29 cm
♀

photo: U. JOST

RT04034-4 *Cathaiemys annamensis* (SIEBENROCK, 1903)

17–29 cm

photo: T. BLANCK

RT04035-4 *Cathaiemys annamensis* (SIEBENROCK, 1903)

17–29 cm
♂

photo: J. MARAN

RT04036-1 *Cathaiemys annamensis* (SIEBENROCK, 1903)

17–29 cm
Hatchling/Schlüpfling

photo: P.P. VAN DIJK

RT04037-4 *Cathaiemys annamensis* (Siebenrock, 1903)
light morph/helle Form
17–29 cm

photo: N. Kawazoe/CREEPER

RT04038-4 *Cathaiemys annamensis* (Siebenrock, 1903)
light morph/helle Form
17–29 cm

photo: T. Blanck

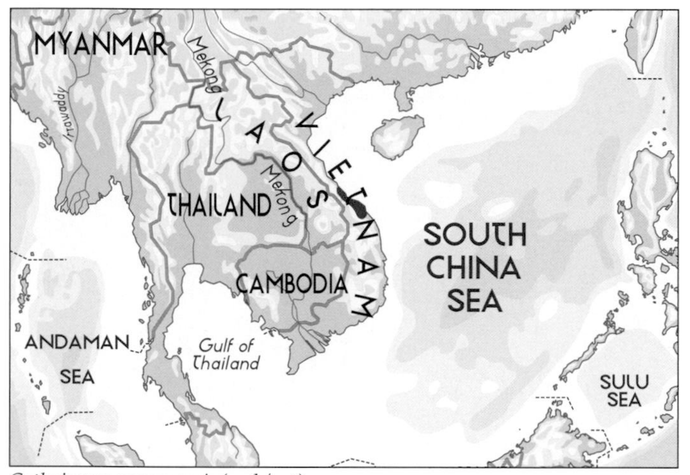

Cathaiemys annamensis (red/rot)

RT04041-4 *Cathaiemys mutica mutica* (Cantor, 1842)

18–20 cm

photo: T. Blanck

RT04042-4 *Cathaiemys mutica mutica* (Cantor, 1842)

18–20 cm

photo: P.P. van Dijk

RT04043-4 *Cathaiemys mutica mutica* (Cantor, 1842)

18–20 cm

photo: T. Blanck

RT04051-4 *Cathaiemys mutica kami* (Yasukawa, Ota & Iverson, 1996)

17–19 cm
♀
photo: J.B. Iverson

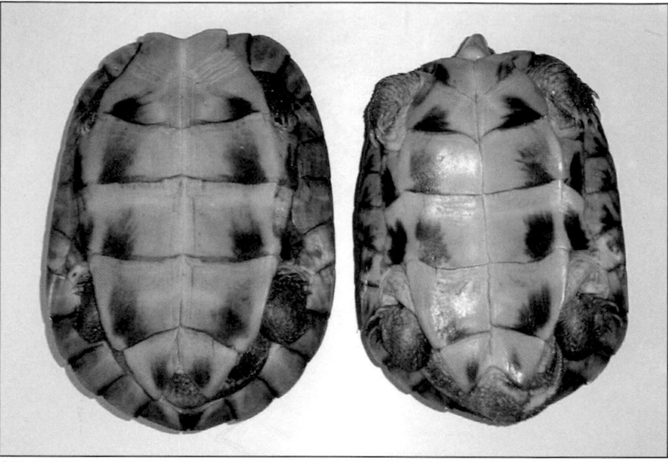

RT04052-4 *Cathaiemys mutica kami* (Yasukawa, Ota & Iverson, 1996)
Iriomote Island, Japan/Insel Iriomote, Japan
17–19 cm
♀ + ♂
photo: P. Petras

RT04053-4 *Cathaiemys mutica kami* (Yasukawa, Ota & Iverson, 1996)

17–19 cm
photo: T. Blanck

RT04054-1 *Cathaiemys mutica kami* (Yasukawa, Ota & Iverson, 1996)
Ishigaki Island, Japan/Insel Ishigaki, Japan
17–19 cm
Hatchling/Schlüpfling
photo: H. Prokop

RT04061-4 *Cathaiemys mutica* "Taiwan form/Taiwan–Form"

18–20 cm
photo: S. Seki

RT04062-1 *Cathaiemys mutica* "Taiwan form/Taiwan–Form"

18–20 cm
Hatchling/Schlüpfling
photo: S. Seki

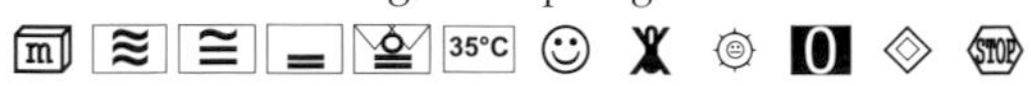

RT04063-4 *Cathaiemys mutica* "Taiwan form / Taiwan–Form"

18–20 cm

photo: S. Seki

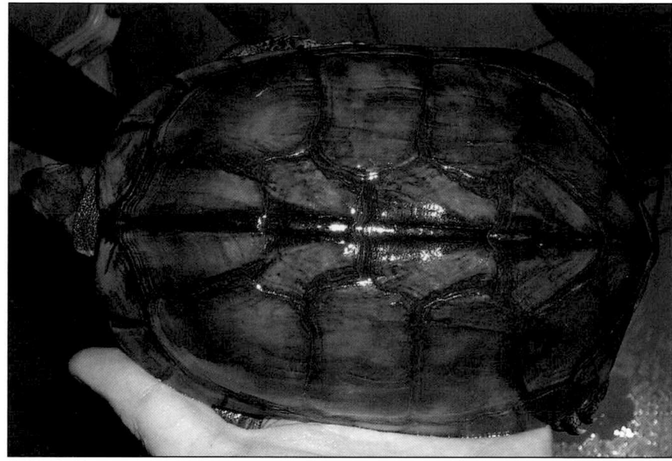

RT04071-4 *Cathaiemys mutica* "Vietnamese form / Vietnamesische Form"

18–26 cm
♂

photo: T. Blanck

Cathaiemys mutica mutica (blue / blau)
Cathaiemys mutica kami (red / rot; arrow / Pfeil)
Cathaiemys mutica "Taiwan form / Taiwan-Form" (orange)
– introduced to Honshu Island (Japan), not depicted here/eingeführt auf der Insel Honshu (Japan), hier nicht abgebildet
Cathaiemys mutica "Vietnamese form / Vietnamesische Form" (green / grün)

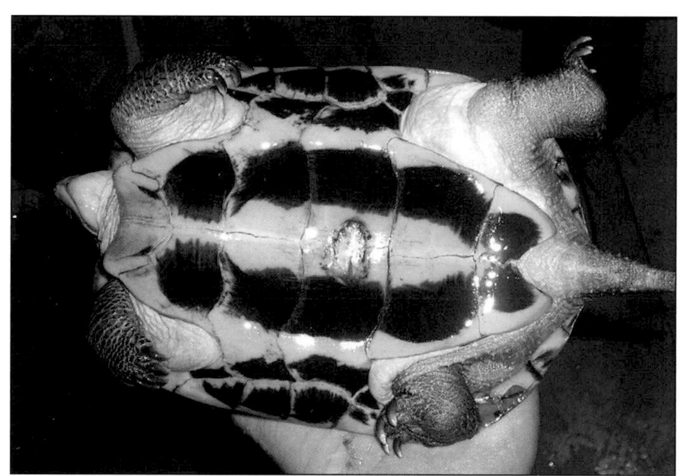

RT04072-4 *Cathaiemys mutica* "Vietnamese form / Vietnamesische Form"

18–26 cm
♂

photo: T. Blanck

RT04073-4 *Cathaiemys mutica* "Vietnamese form / Vietnamesische Form"

18–26 cm
♂

photo: T. Blanck

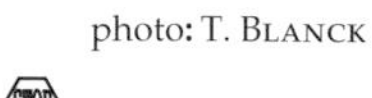

RT04081-4 *Chinemys megalocephala* Fang, 1934

20–23 cm

photo: J.H. Harding

RT04082-4 *Chinemys megalocephala* Fang, 1934

20–23 cm

photo: P. Petras

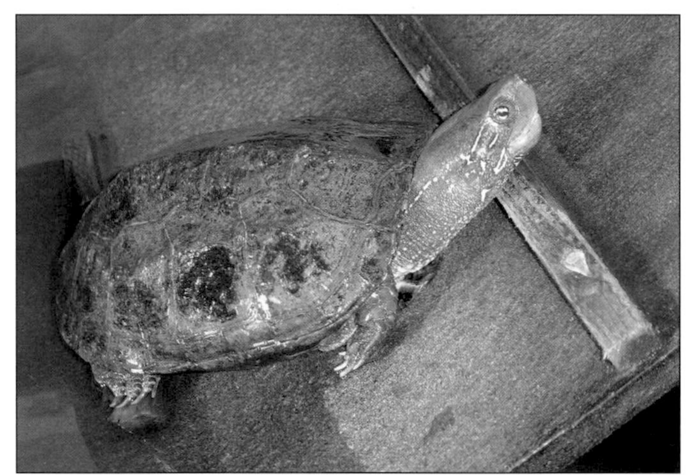

RT04083-4 *Chinemys megalocephala* Fang, 1934
Fukuoka, Kyushu, Japan
20–23 cm
♀

photo: P. Petras

RT04084-4 *Chinemys megalocephala* Fang, 1934

20–23 cm
♀

photo: T. Blanck

RT04091-4 *Chinemys nigricans* (Gray, 1834)

25–30 cm
♀

photo: T. Blanck

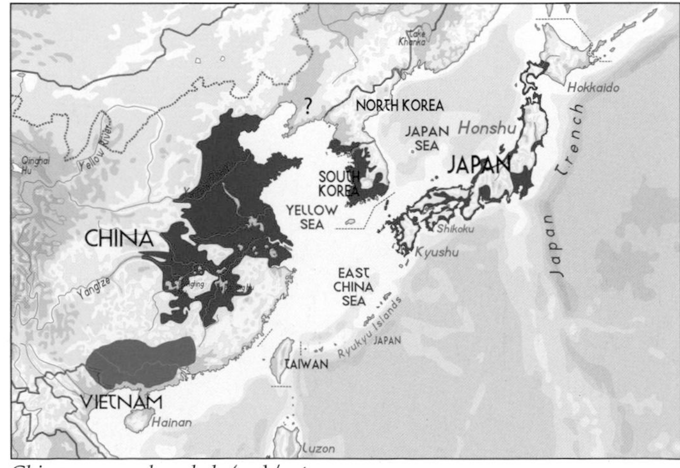

Chinemys megalocephala (red / rot;
?: questionable occurrence / Vorkommen fraglich)
Chinemys nigricans (blue / blau)

RT04092-4 *Chinemys nigricans* (Gray, 1834)

25–30 cm
♀
photo: B. Wolff

RT04093-4 *Chinemys nigricans* (Gray, 1834)

25–30 cm
♂ + ♀
photo: J. Maran

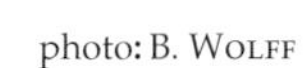

RT04094-4 *Chinemys nigricans* (Gray, 1834)

25–30 cm
♂
photo: J.B. Iverson

RT04095-4 *Chinemys nigricans* (Gray, 1834)

25–30 cm
♀
photo: T. Blanck

RT04096-1 *Chinemys nigricans* (Gray, 1834)

25–30 cm
Hatching/Schlupf
photo: J. Maran

RT04097-2 *Chinemys nigricans* (Gray, 1834)

25–30 cm
Juvenile/Jungtier
photo: J.H. Harding

RT0XXXX-1 *Chinemys reevesii* (Gray, 1831)
13–24 cm
♀
photo: J. Maran

RT0XXXX-1 *Chinemys reevesii* (Gray, 1831)
13–24 cm
♀
photo: P.P. van Dijk

RT0XXXX-1 *Chinemys reevesii* (Gray, 1831)
13–24 cm
photo: O. Born

RT0XXXX-1 *Chinemys reevesii* (Gray, 1831)
13–24 cm
♀
photo: S. Pawlowski

RT0XXXX-1 *Chinemys reevesii* (Gray, 1831)
13–24 cm
Juvenile/Jungtier
photo: S. Pawlowski

NORTH KOREA
JAPAN SEA
Honshu
JAPAN
Hokkaido
Japan Trench
SOUTH KOREA
CHINA
YELLOW SEA
Yellow River
Shikoku
Kyushu
EAST CHINA SEA
Ryukyu Islands
TAIWAN
Hainan
Luzon
Mekong

Chinemys reevesii (red/rot)
– introduced to Okinawa (Japan), Timor (Indonesia), Singapore and East Timor, not depicted here/ eingeführt auf Okinawa (Japan), Timor (Indonesien), in Singapur und Timor Leste, hier nicht abgebildet

RT04111-4 *Cistoclemmys bourreti* (Fritz & Reimann, 1994)

16–18 cm

photo: J. Maran

RT04112-4 *Cistoclemmys bourreti* (Fritz & Reimann, 1994)

16–18 cm
♀

photo: T. Blanck

RT04113-4 *Cistoclemmys bourreti* (Fritz & Reimann, 1994)

16–18 cm

photo: S. Szymanski

RT04114-4 *Cistoclemmys bourreti* (Fritz & Reimann, 1994)

16–18 cm
♂

photo: S. Szymanski

RT04115-4 *Cistoclemmys bourreti* (Fritz & Reimann, 1994)
Cambodia / Kambodscha
16–18 cm

photo: T. Blanck

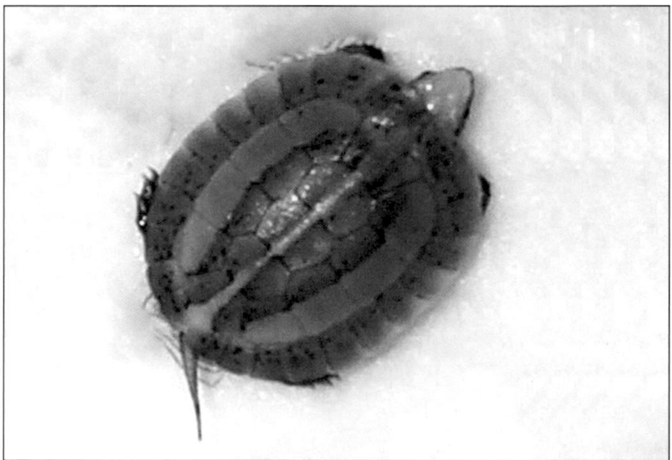

RT04116-1 *Cistoclemmys bourreti* (Fritz & Reimann, 1994)

16–18 cm
Hatchling / Schlüpfling

photo: K. + W. Heuberger

RT04121-4 *Cistoclemmys flavomarginata flavomarginata* GRAY, 1863

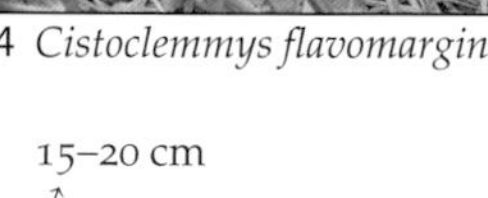

15–20 cm
♂
photo: S. PAWLOWSKI

RT04122-4 *Cistoclemmys flavomarginata flavomarginata* GRAY, 1863

15–20 cm
♂
photo: P.P. VAN DIJK

RT04123-1 *Cistoclemmys flavomarginata flavomarginata* GRAY, 1863

15–20 cm
Hatching/Schlupf
photo: S. PAWLOWSKI

RT04131-2 *Cistoclemmys flavomarginata evelynae* (ERNST & LOVICH, 1990)

15–17 cm
Juvenile/Jungtier
photo: T. BERNDT/A. MENDE

RT04132-4 *Cistoclemmys flavomarginata evelynae* (ERNST & LOVICH, 1990)

15–17 cm
photo: T. BERNDT/A. MENDE

RT04133-4 *Cistoclemmys flavomarginata evelynae* (ERNST & LOVICH, 1990)

15–17 cm
photo: T. BERNDT/A. MENDE

Cistoclemmys bourreti (blue/blau); *Cistoclemmys flavomarginata flavomarginata* (green/grün); *Cistoclemmys flavomarginata evelynae* (red/rot; arrow/Pfeil)
Cistoclemmys flavomarginata sinensis (yellow/gelb) – introduced to Hong Kong (China), not depicted here/eingeführt in Honkong (China), hier nicht abgebildet
Cistoclemmys galbinifrons (brown/braun); *Cistoclemmys mccordi* (orange); *Cistoclemmys picturata* (purple/lila);
areas of intergradation/Intergradationszonen (pink); ?: questionable occurrence/Vorkommen fraglich)

RT04134-4 *Cistoclemmys flavomarginata evelynae* (Ernst & Lovich, 1990)

15–17 cm

photo: T. Berndt/A. Mende

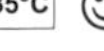

RT04141-4 *Cistoclemmys flavomarginata sinensis* (Hsü, 1930)

15–20 cm

photo: J.B. Iverson

RT04142-4 *Cistoclemmys flavomarginata sinensis* (Hsü, 1930)

15–20 cm

photo: J.B. Iverson

RT04143-4 *Cistoclemmys flavomarginata sinensis* (Hsü, 1930)

15–20 cm

photo: J.B. Iverson

RT04151-4 *Cistoclemmys galbinifrons* (Bourret, 1939)
Vietnam
18–20 cm
♂

photo: J. Maran

RT04152-4 *Cistoclemmys galbinifrons* (Bourret, 1939)
Vietnam
18–20 cm

photo: J. Maran

RT04153-4 *Cistoclemmys galbinifrons* (Bourret, 1939)

18–20 cm

photo: S. Szymanski

RT04154-4 *Cistoclemmys galbinifrons* (Bourret, 1939)
Vietnam
18–20 cm

photo: J. Maran

RT04155-4 *Cistoclemmys galbinifrons* (BOURRET, 1939)
Vietnam
18–20 cm
photo: J. MARAN

RT04156-4 *Cistoclemmys galbinifrons* (BOURRET, 1939)
18–20 cm
photo: T. BLANCK

RT04161-4 *Cistoclemmys mccordi* (ERNST, 1988)
12–15 cm
photo: A. NÖLLERT

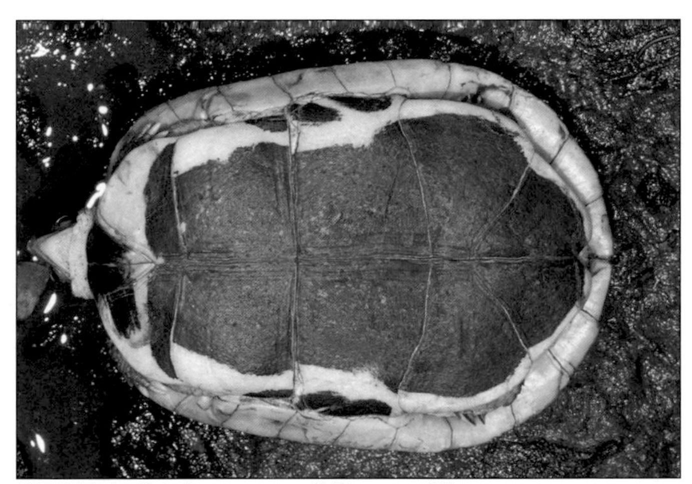

RT04162-4 *Cistoclemmys mccordi* (ERNST, 1988)
12–15 cm
photo: A. NÖLLERT

RT04163-4 *Cistoclemmys mccordi* (ERNST, 1988)
12–15 cm
♀
photo: T. BLANCK

RT04164-4 *Cistoclemmys mccordi* (ERNST, 1988)
12–15 cm
photo: J.H. HARDING

RT04165-1 *Cistoclemmys mccordi* (ERNST, 1988)

12–15 cm
Hatchling/Schlüpfling
photo: A. NÖLLERT

RT04166-1 *Cistoclemmys mccordi* (ERNST, 1988)

12–15 cm
Hatchling/Schlüpfling
photo: A. NÖLLERT

RT04171-4 *Cistoclemmys picturata* (LEHR, FRITZ & OBST, 1998)
light morph/helle Form
16–18 cm
♀
photo: T. BLANCK

RT04172-4 *Cistoclemmys picturata* (LEHR, FRITZ & OBST, 1998)

16–18 cm
♀
photo: T. BERNDT/A. MENDE

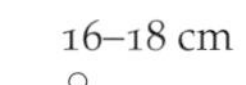    

RT04174-4 *Cistoclemmys picturata* (LEHR, FRITZ & OBST, 1998)
dark morph/dunkle Form
16–18 cm
♀
photo: J. MARAN

RT04175-4 *Cistoclemmys picturata* (LEHR, FRITZ & OBST, 1998)

16–18 cm
♀
photo: T. BERNDT/A. MENDE

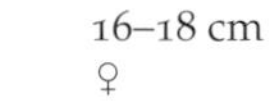    

RT04181-4 *Cuora amboinensis amboinensis* (DAUDIN, 1801)

20–22 cm
♀

photo: M. KOCH

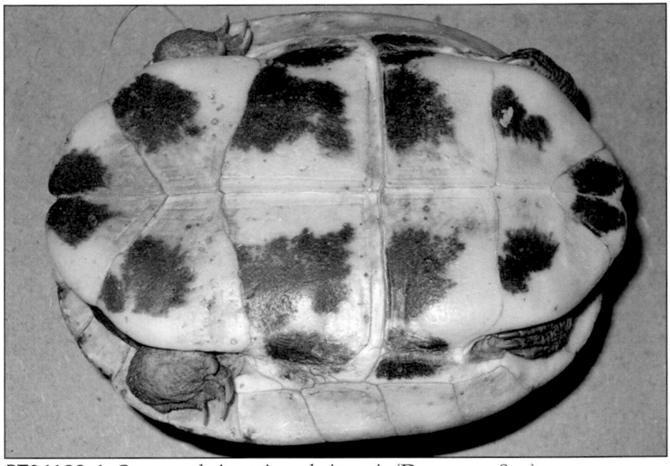

RT04182-4 *Cuora amboinensis amboinensis* (DAUDIN, 1801)

20–22 cm
♀

photo: M. KOCH

RT04183-4 *Cuora amboinensis amboinensis* (DAUDIN, 1801)
Kotamobagu , Sulawesi, Indonesia/Indonesien
20–22 cm

photo: A. KOCH

RT04184-4 *Cuora amboinensis amboinensis* (DAUDIN, 1801)
Kotamobagu , Sulawesi, Indonesia/Indonesien
20–22 cm

photo: A. KOCH

RT04185-4 *Cuora amboinensis amboinensis* (DAUDIN, 1801)
Sulawesi, Indonesia/Indonesien
20–22 cm

photo: T. BLANCK

RT04191-4 *Cuora amboinensis couro* (SCHWEIGGER, 1812)
Java, Indonesia/Indonesien
20–22 cm

photo: D. TROBISCH

RT04192-4 *Cuora amboinensis couro* (Schweigger, 1812)

20–22 cm

photo: B. Esser

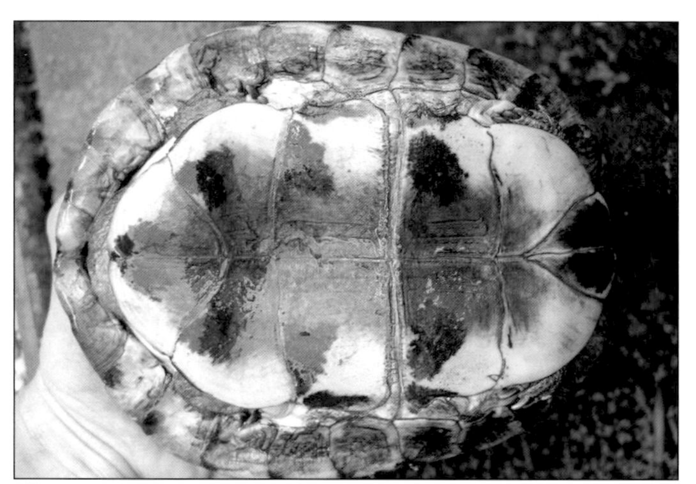

RT04193-4 *Cuora amboinensis couro* (Schweigger, 1812)

20–22 cm

photo: B. Esser

RT04194-4 *Cuora amboinensis couro* (Schweigger, 1812)
Java, Indonesia / Indonesien
20–22 cm

photo: D. Trobisch

RT04201-4 *Cuora amboinensis kamaroma* Rummler & Fritz, 1991
Vietnam
20–22 cm

photo: J. Maran

RT04202-4 *Cuora amboinensis kamaroma* Rummler & Fritz, 1991
Vietnam
20–22 cm

photo: J. Maran

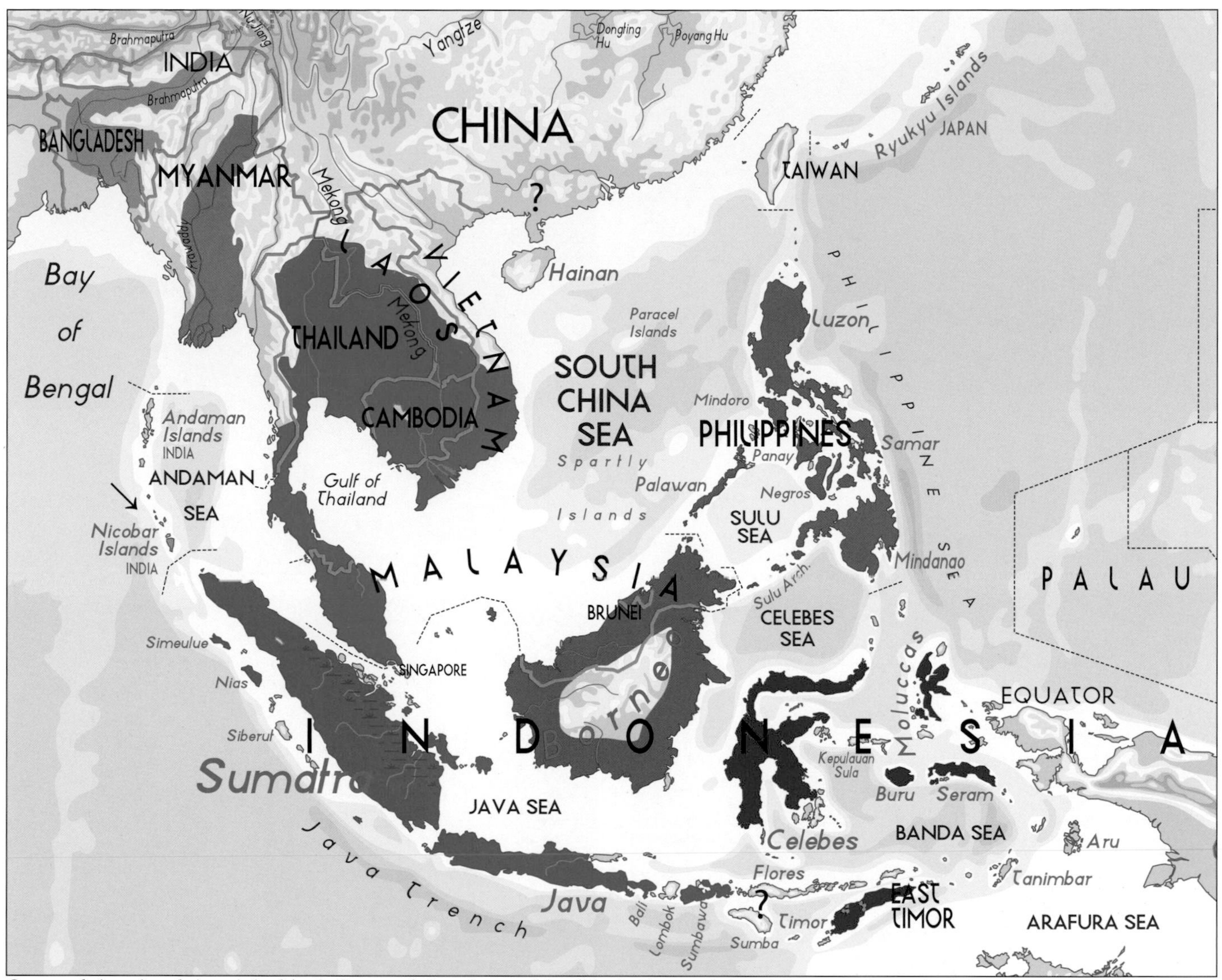

Cuora amboinensis amboinensis (red / rot); *Cuora amboinensis couro* (blue / blau); *Cuora amboinensis kamaroma* (green / grün)
Cuora amboinensis lineata (pink); *Cuora amboinensis* "Borneo form / Borneo-Form" (brown / braun)
Cuora amboinensis "Indian form / Indische Form" (gray / grau); *Cuora amboinensis* "Nicobar form / Nikobaren-Form" (orange; arrow / Pfeil),
Cuora amboinensis "Philippine form / Philippinen-Form" (purple / lila)
?: questionable occurrence / Vorkommen fraglich

RT04203-4 *Cuora amboinensis kamaroma* Rummler & Fritz, 1991
Huai Kha Khaeng, Uthai Thani, Thailand
20–22 cm

photo: P.P. van Dijk

RT04204 *Cuora amboinensis kamaroma* Rummler & Fritz, 1991
Habitat, Paddyfields in Peninsular Thailand

photo: P.P. van Dijk

RT04211-4 *Cuora amboinensis lineata* McCord & Philippen, 1998

20–22 cm
♂
photo: M. Koch

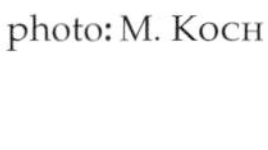

RT04212-4 *Cuora amboinensis lineata* McCord & Philippen, 1998

20–22 cm
♀
photo: M. Koch

RT04221-4 *Cuora amboinensis* "Borneo form/Borneo–Form"
Mundanao lake, vicinity Taytay, Palawan, Philippines/
Mundanao-See, Gegend von Taytay, Palawan, Philippinen
20–22 cm photo: P. Petras + H. Prokop

RT04222-4 *Cuora amboinensis* "Borneo form/Borneo–Form"
Mundanao lake, vicinity Taytay, Palawan, Philippines/
Mundanao-See, Gegend von Taytay, Palawan, Philippinen
20–22 cm photo: P. Petras + H. Prokop

RT04223-4 *Cuora amboinensis* "Borneo form/Borneo–Form"
Mundanao lake, vicinity Taytay, Palawan, Philippines/
Mundanao-See, Gegend von Taytay, Palawan, Philippinen
20–22 cm photo: P. Petras + H. Prokop

RT04224-4 *Cuora amboinensis* "Borneo form/Borneo–Form"
West Kalimantan, Borneo, Indonesia/Indonesien
20–22 cm
photo: M. Auliya

RT04225 *Cuora amboinensis* "Borneo form / Borneo–Form"
Mundanao lake, vicinity Taytay, Palawan, Philippines
Mundanao-See, Gegend von Taytay, Palawan, Philippinen
Habitat photo: P. PETRAS + H. PROKOP

RT04231 *Cuora amboinensis* "Indian form / Indische Form"
Habitat, Assam, India / Indien
photo: P. PRASCHAG

RT04241-4 *Cuora amboinensis* "Nicobar form / Nikobaren–Form"
Great Nicobar Island, India / Insel Great Nicobar, Indien
20–22 cm
photo: I. DAS

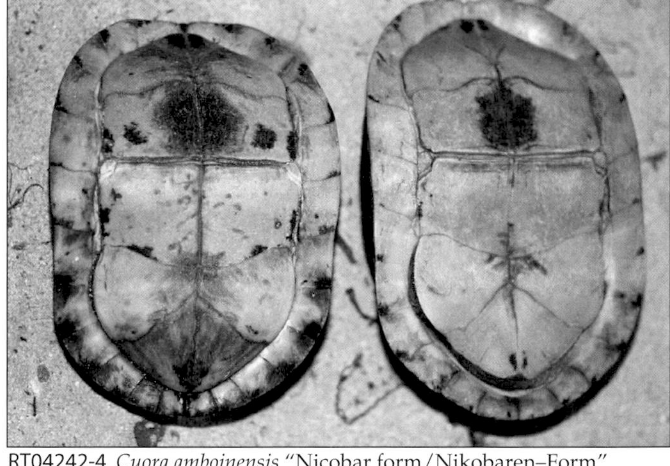

RT04242-4 *Cuora amboinensis* "Nicobar form / Nikobaren–Form"
Great Nicobar Island, India / Insel Great Nicobar, Indien
20–22 cm
photo: I. DAS

RT04251-4 *Cuora amboinensis* "Philippine form / Philippinen–Form"
Leyte Island, Philippines / Insel Leyte, Philippinen
20–22 cm
photo: T. BLANCK

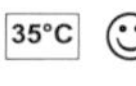

RT04252-4 *Cuora amboinensis* "Philippine form / Philippinen–Form"
Leyte Island, Philippines / Insel Leyte, Philippinen
20–22 cm
photo: T. BLANCK

RT04261-4 *Cyclemys atripons atripons* Iverson & McCord, 1997

20–23 cm

photo: M. Schilde

RT04262-4 *Cyclemys atripons atripons* Iverson & McCord, 1997

20–23 cm

photo: M. Schilde

RT04263-4 *Cyclemys atripons atripons* Iverson & McCord, 1997
Botum Sakor NP, S Cambodia/S Kambodscha
20–23 cm

photo: D. Emmett

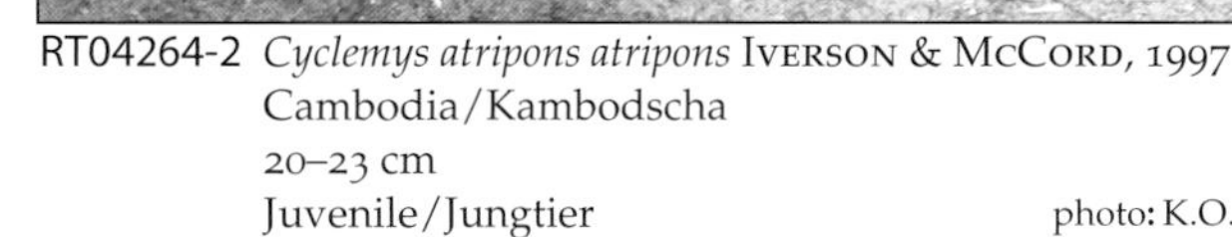

RT04264-2 *Cyclemys atripons atripons* Iverson & McCord, 1997
Cambodia/Kambodscha
20–23 cm
Juvenile/Jungtier

photo: K.O. Krüger

RT04271-4 *Cyclemys atripons pulchristriata* Fritz, Gaulke & Lehr, 1997

17–19 cm

photo: T. Blanck

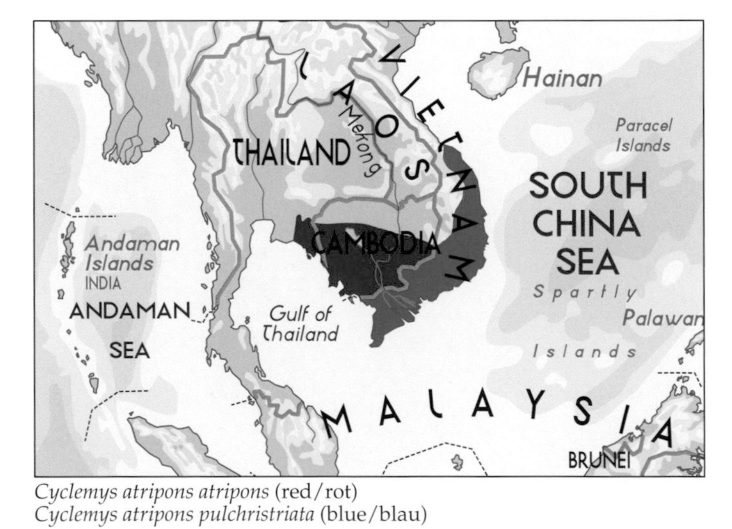

Cyclemys atripons atripons (red/rot)
Cyclemys atripons pulchristriata (blue/blau)

RT04272-4 *Cyclemys atripons pulchristriata* Fritz, Gaulke & Lehr, 1997
Vietnam
17–19 cm
photo: J. Maran

RT04273-4 *Cyclemys atripons pulchristriata* Fritz, Gaulke & Lehr, 1997
Vietnam
17–19 cm
♂ + ♀
photo: J. Maran

RT04281-4 *Cyclemys dentata* (Gray, 1831)

24–26 cm
♂
photo: M. Koch

RT04282-4 *Cyclemys dentata* (Gray, 1831)

24–26 cm
♀
photo: M. Koch

RT04283-4 *Cyclemys dentata* (Gray, 1831)

24–26 cm
♀
photo: M. Koch

RT04284-2 *Cyclemys dentata* (Gray, 1831)

24–26 cm
Juvenile/Jungtier
photo: N. Kawazoe/CREEPER

Cyclemys dentata (red/rot)

Cyclemys oldhamii (red/rot)

RT04291-4 *Cyclemys oldhamii* Gray, 1863
Bandar Seri Begawan, Brunei
19–22 cm

photo: I. Das

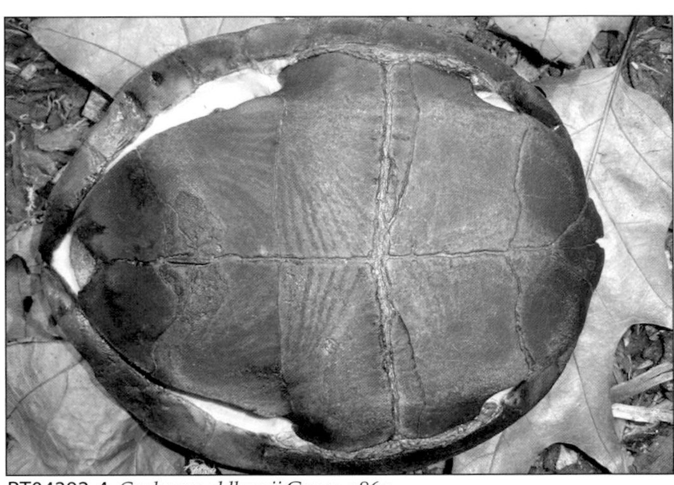

RT04292-4 *Cyclemys oldhamii* Gray, 1863

19–22 cm

photo: P. Petras

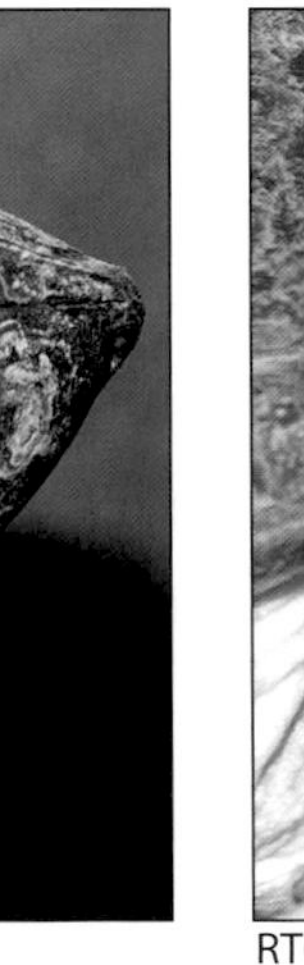

RT04293-4 *Cyclemys oldhamii* Gray, 1863

19–22 cm
♂

photo: M. Koch

RT04294-4 *Cyclemys oldhamii* Gray, 1863

19–22 cm
♀

photo: M. Koch

RT04295-4 *Cyclemys oldhamii* Gray, 1863
West Kalimantan, Borneo, Indonesia/Indonesien
19–22 cm
photo: M. Auliya

RT04301-2 *Cyclemys ovata* Gray, 1863
West Kalimantan, Borneo, Indonesia/Indonesien
24–26 cm
Juvenile/Jungtier
photo: M. Auliya

RT04302-4 *Cyclemys ovata* Gray, 1863
Sarawak, Malaysia
24–26 cm
photo: I. Das

RT04303-4 *Cyclemys ovata* Gray, 1863
Sarawak, Malaysia
24–26 cm
photo: I. Das

RT04304-4 *Cyclemys ovata* Gray, 1863
Sarawak, Malaysia
24–26 cm
photo: I. Das

RT04305-4 *Cyclemys ovata* Gray, 1863
24–26 cm
photo: N. Kawazoe/CREEPER

RT04311-4 *Cyclemys shanensis shanensis* ANNANDALE, 1918

18–23 cm
♂
photo: M. KOCH

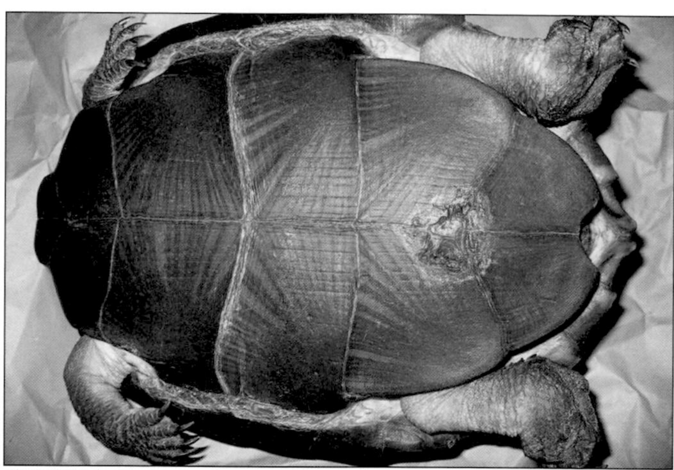
RT04312-4 *Cyclemys shanensis shanensis* ANNANDALE, 1918

18–23 cm
♀
photo: M. KOCH

RT04321-4 *Cyclemys shanensis tcheponensis* (BOURRET, 1939)

18–20 cm
♀
photo: J. MARAN

RT04322-4 *Cyclemys shanensis tcheponensis* (BOURRET, 1939)

18–20 cm
♀
photo: J. MARAN

RT04323-4 *Cyclemys shanensis tcheponensis* (BOURRET, 1939)

18–20 cm
photo: M. SCHILDE

RT04324-2 *Cyclemys shanensis tcheponensis* (BOURRET, 1939)

18–20 cm
Juvenile/Jungtier
photo: U. THIEME

Cyclemys ovata (red/rot); *Cyclemys shanensis shanensis (blue/blau)*
Cyclemys shanensis tcheponensis (orange)
Cyclemys "Cambodian form/Kambodschanische Form" (green/grün)
Cyclemys "Indian form/Indische Form" (purple/lila)
Cyclemys "Java form/Java-Form" (brown/braun)
Cyclemys "Kachin form/Kachin-Form" (pink)

RT04331-4 *Cyclemys* "Indian form/Indische Form"
Nhengpui, Mizoram, India/Indien
19–22 cm

photo: S. Mukherjee

RT04351-4 *Cyclemys* "Java form/Java–Form"
SE Java, Indonesia/SO- Java, Indonesien
24–26 cm

photo: D. Trobisch

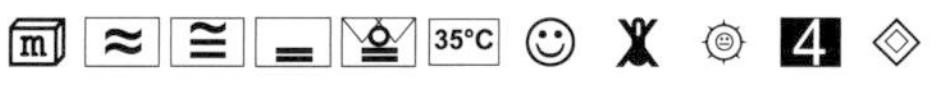

RT04361-4 *Cyclemys* "Kachin form/Kachin–Form"
Chindwin, N Myanmar
19–22 cm

photo: G. Kuchling

RT04362-4 *Cyclemys* "Kachin form/Kachin–Form"
Chindwin, N Myanmar
19–22 cm

photo: G. Kuchling

RT04371-4 *Geoclemys hamiltonii* (GRAY, 1831)

35–40 cm
♀

photo: F. WÜTHRICH

RT04372-4 *Geoclemys hamiltonii* (GRAY, 1831)
Bangladesh/Bangladesch
35–40 cm

photo: P. PRASCHAG

RT04373-4 *Geoclemys hamiltonii* (GRAY, 1831)
Kukrail, Uttar Pradesh, India/Indien
35–40 cm

photo: P. P. VAN DIJK

RT04374-4 *Geoclemys hamiltonii* (GRAY, 1831)

35–40 cm

photo: J. MARAN

RT04375-4 *Geoclemys hamiltonii* (GRAY, 1831)

35–40 cm
♀

photo: J.B. IVERSON

RT04376-1 *Geoclemys hamiltonii* (GRAY, 1831)

35–40 cm
Hatchling/Schlüpfling

photo: G. SCHAFFER

RT04377-4 *Geoclemys hamiltonii* (GRAY, 1831)

35–40 cm
♀

photo: J.B. IVERSON

RT04378 *Geoclemys hamiltonii* (GRAY, 1831)
Habitat, Dudwa NP, Uttar Pradesh, India/Indien

photo: P. P. VAN DIJK

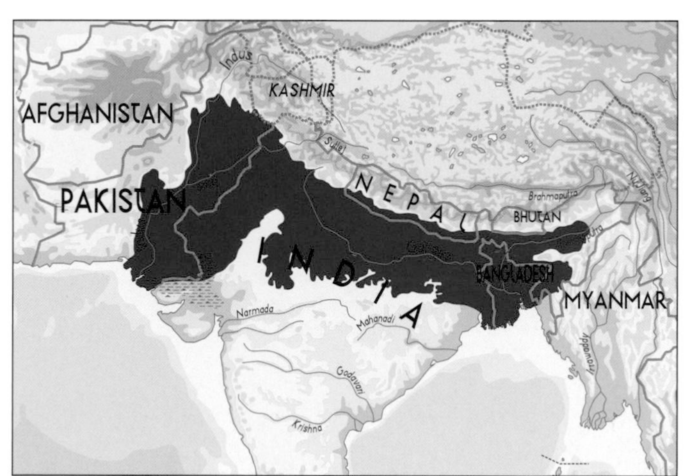

Geoclemys hamiltonii (red/rot)

RT04381-4 *Geoemyda japonica* FAN, 1931

15–17 cm
♀

photo: J.H. HARDING

RT04382-4 *Geoemyda japonica* FAN, 1931

15–17 cm
♂

photo: T. BLANCK

RT04383-4 *Geoemyda japonica* FAN, 1931

15–17 cm

photo: T. BLANCK

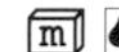

RT04384-2 *Geoemyda japonica* FAN, 1931
Okinawa Island, Japan/Insel Okinawa, Japan
15–17 cm
Juvenile/Jungtier
photo: N. KAWAZOE/CREEPER

 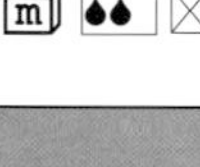   

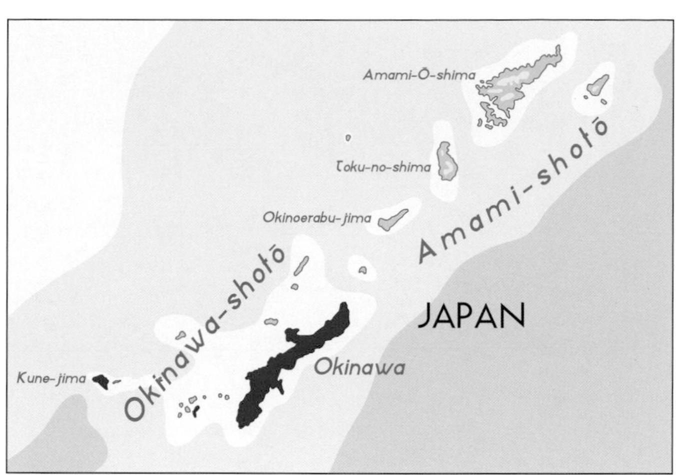

Geoemyda japonica (red/rot)

RT04391-4 *Geoemyda spengleri* (GMELIN, 1789)

9–13 cm
♂
photo: P. P. VAN DIJK

RT04392-4 *Geoemyda spengleri* (GMELIN, 1789)

9–13 cm
♀
photo: S. PAWLOWSKI

RT04393-4 *Geoemyda spengleri* (GMELIN, 1789)
Guangxi, China
9–13 cm
photo: T. BLANCK

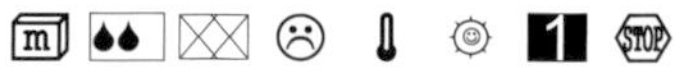        

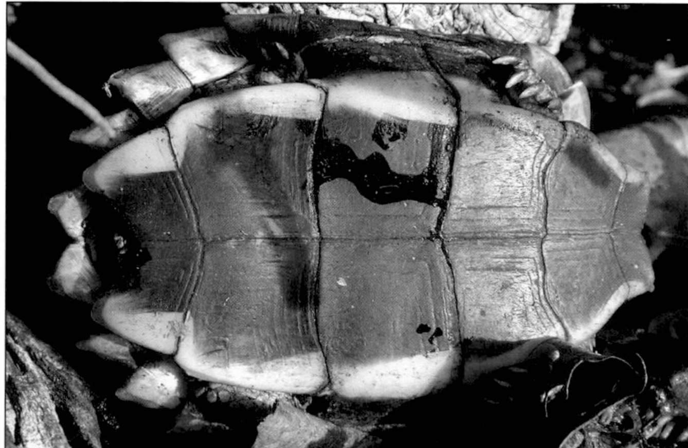

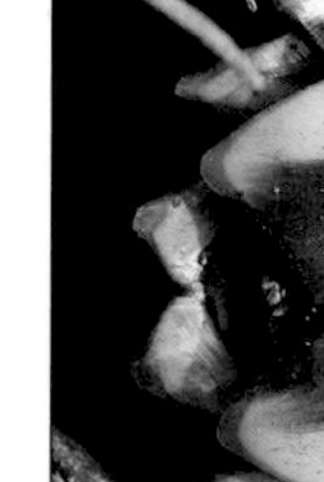

RT04394-4 *Geoemyda spengleri* (GMELIN, 1789)

9–13 cm
♀
photo: F. WÜTHRICH

RT04395-4 *Geoemyda spengleri* (GMELIN, 1789)

9–13 cm
♂

photo: M. ROGNER

RT04396-4 *Geoemyda spengleri* (GMELIN, 1789)

9–13 cm

photo: F. WÜTHRICH

RT04397-2 *Geoemyda spengleri* (GMELIN, 1789)

9–13 cm
Juvenile/Jungtier

photo: N. KAWAZOE/CREEPER

RT04398 *Geoemyda spengleri* (GMELIN, 1789)
Habitat, Tam Dao, Vietnam

photo: P.P. VAN DIJK

Geoemyda spengleri (red/rot;
?: questionable occurrence/Vorkommen fraglich)

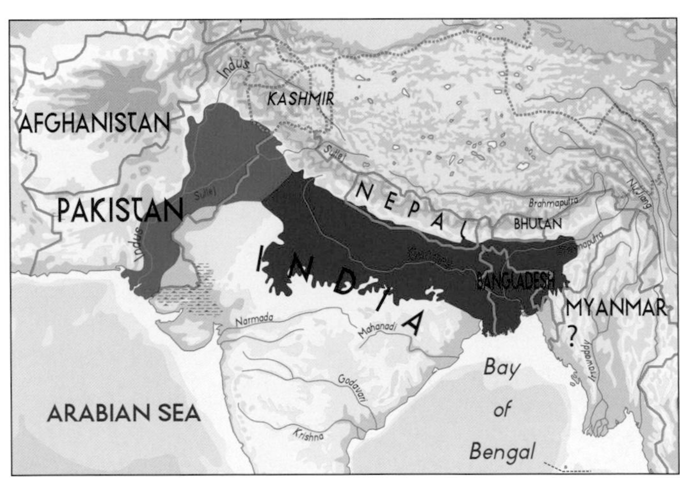

Hardella thurjii thurjii (red/rot;
?: questionable occurrence/Vorkommen fraglich)
Hardella thurjii indi (blue/blau)

RT04401-4 *Hardella thurjii thurjii* (GRAY, 1831)
Chambal River, Madhya Pradesh, India/Indien
18–61 cm
photo: I. DAS

RT04402-4 *Hardella thurjii thurjii* (GRAY, 1831)
Kukrail, Uttar Pradesh, India/Indien
18–61 cm
♀
photo: P.P. VAN DIJK

RT04403-4 *Hardella thurjii thurjii* (GRAY, 1831)
Kukrail, Uttar Pradesh, India/Indien
18–61 cm
♀
photo: P.P. VAN DIJK

RT04411-4 *Hardella thurjii indi* GRAY, 1870
Pakistan
18–61 cm
photo: R. PRASCHAG

RT04412-4 *Hardella thurjii indi* GRAY, 1870
Pakistan
18–61 cm
photo: R. PRASCHAG

RT04413-4 *Hardella thurjii indi* GRAY, 1870
Pakistan
18–61 cm
photo: K.H. SWITAK

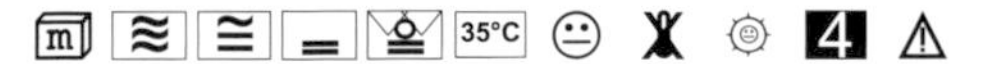

RT04421-4 *Heosemys depressa* (ANDERSON, 1875)

25–27 cm

photo: B. WOLFF

RT04422-4 *Heosemys depressa* (ANDERSON, 1875)

25–27 cm
♂ + ♀

photo: J. MARAN

RT04423-4 *Heosemys depressa* (ANDERSON, 1875)

25–27 cm
♀

photo: J. MARAN

RT04424-4 *Heosemys depressa* (ANDERSON, 1875)

25–27 cm

photo: P. PETRAS

RT04425-2 *Heosemys depressa* (ANDERSON, 1875)
Atlanta Zoo, USA
25–27 cm
Juvenile/Jungtier

photo: H.-D. PHILIPPEN

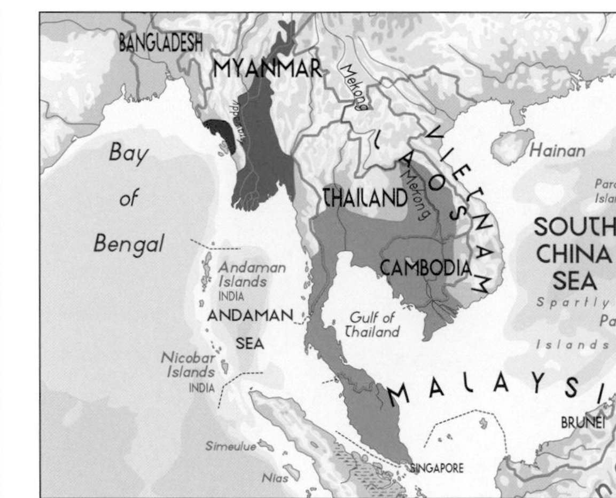

Heosemys depressa (red/rot)
Heosemys grandis "Myanmar form/Myanmar-Form" (blue/blau)
Heosemys grandis "Southern form/Südliche Forme" (orange)

RT04431-4 *Heosemys grandis* (Gray, 1860)
"Myanmar form/Myanmar–Form"
40–44 cm

photo: S. Seki

RT04432-4 *Heosemys grandis* (Gray, 1860)
"Myanmar form/Myanmar–Form"
40–44 cm

photo: W.P. McCord

RT04441-4 *Heosemys grandis* (Gray, 1860) "Southern form/Südliche Form"

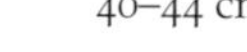

40–44 cm

photo: O. Born

RT04442-4 *Heosemys grandis* (Gray, 1860) "Southern form/Südliche Form"
Vietnam
40–44 cm
♂ + ♀

photo: J. Maran

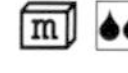

RT04443-4 *Heosemys grandis* (Gray, 1860) "Southern form/Südliche Form"

40–44 cm
♀

photo: T. Berndt/A. Mende

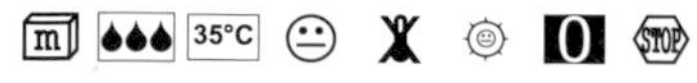

RT04444-4 *Heosemys grandis* (Gray, 1860) "Southern form/Südliche Form"

40–44 cm

photo: J. Maran

RT04445-4 *Heosemys grandis* (GRAY, 1860) "Southern form/Südliche Form"

40–44 cm
♂

photo: T. BERNDT/A. MENDE

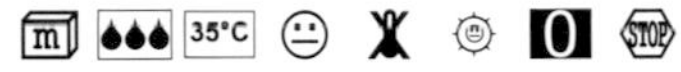

RT04446-4 *Heosemys grandis* (GRAY, 1860) "Southern form/Südliche Form"

40–44 cm

photo: J. MARAN

RT04447-1 *Heosemys grandis* (GRAY, 1860) "Southern form/Südliche Form"

40–44 cm
Hatching/Schlupf

photo: J. MARAN

Heosemys spinosa "Insular form/Insel-Form" (red/rot)
Heosemys spinosa "Mainland form/Festland-Form" (blue/blau)

RT04448-2 *Heosemys grandis* (GRAY, 1860) "Southern form/Südliche Form"

40–44 cm
Juvenile/Jungtier

photo: A. NÖLLERT

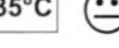

RT04451-4 *Heosemys spinosa* (GRAY, 1831) "Insular form/Insel-Form"
West Kalimantan, Borneo, Indonesia/Indonesien
18–23 cm

photo: M. AULIYA

RT04461-4 *Heosemys spinosa* (Gray, 1831)
"Mainland form/Festland–Form"
18–23 cm
♂
photo: J. Maran

RT04462-4 *Heosemys spinosa* (Gray, 1831)
"Mainland form/Festland–Form"
18–23 cm
photo: J. Maran

RT04463-4 *Heosemys spinosa* (Gray, 1831)
"Mainland form/Festland–Form"
18–23 cm
♂ + ♀
photo: J. Maran

RT04464-4 *Heosemys spinosa* (Gray, 1831)
"Mainland form/Festland–Form"
18–23 cm
♂
photo: T. Berndt/A. Mende

RT04465-2 *Heosemys spinosa* (Gray, 1831)
"Mainland form/Festland–Form"
18–23 cm
Juvenile/Jungtier
photo: H.-D. Philippen

RT04466-4 *Heosemys spinosa* (Gray, 1831)
"Mainland form/Festland–Form",
Johor, Malaysia
18–23 cm
photo: I. Das

RT04471-4 *Hieremys annandalii* (Boulenger, 1903)

45–51 cm

photo: P.P. van Dijk

RT04472-4 *Hieremys annandalii* (Boulenger, 1903)

45–51 cm

photo: G. Schaffer

RT04473-4 *Hieremys annandalii* (Boulenger, 1903)
Bangkok, Thailand
45–51 cm

photo: P.P. van Dijk

RT04474-4 *Hieremys annandalii* (Boulenger, 1903)

45–51 cm

photo: M. Schilde

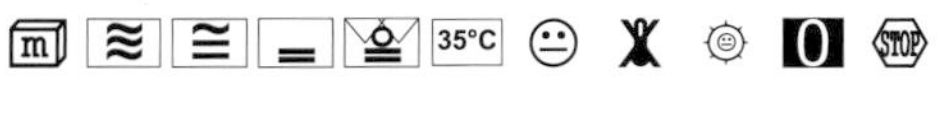

RT04475-4 *Hieremys annandalii* (Boulenger, 1903)

45–51 cm

photo: J. Maran

RT04476-2 *Hieremys annandalii* (Boulenger, 1903)

45–51 cm
Juvenile/Jungtier

photo: H. Prokop

RT04477-1 *Hieremys annandalii* (BOULENGER, 1903)
Bangkok, Thailand
45–51 cm
Hatchling/Schlüpfling
photo: P.P. VAN DIJK

RT04478-1 *Hieremys annandalii* (BOULENGER, 1903)
Cambodia/Kambodscha
45–51 cm
Hatchling/Schlüpfling
photo: S. SZYMANSKI

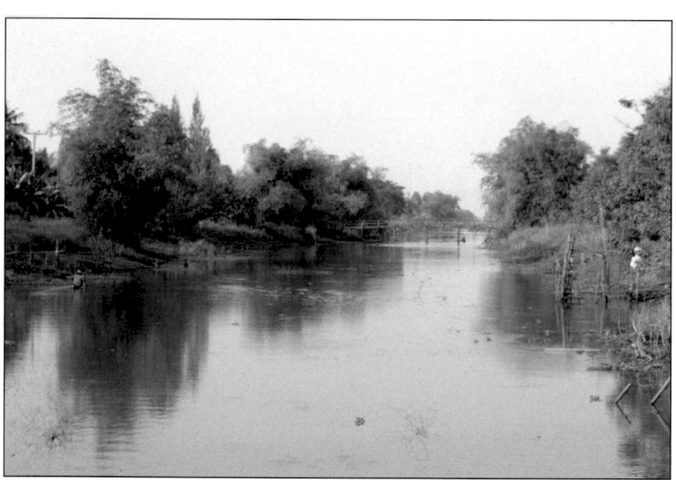

RT04479 *Hieremys annandalii* (BOULENGER, 1903)
Habitat, Rangsit, Pathum Thain, Thailand
photo: P.P. VAN DIJK

RT04470-1 *Hieremys annandalii* (BOULENGER, 1903)
Cambodia/Kambodscha
45–51 cm
Hatchling/Schlüpfling
photo: S. SZYMANSKI

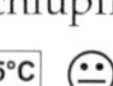

RT0447X *Hieremys annandalii* (BOULENGER, 1903)
Temple pond of Wat Prayoon, Bangkok/
Tempelteich in Wat Prayoon, Bangkok, Thailand
photo: P.P. VAN DIJK

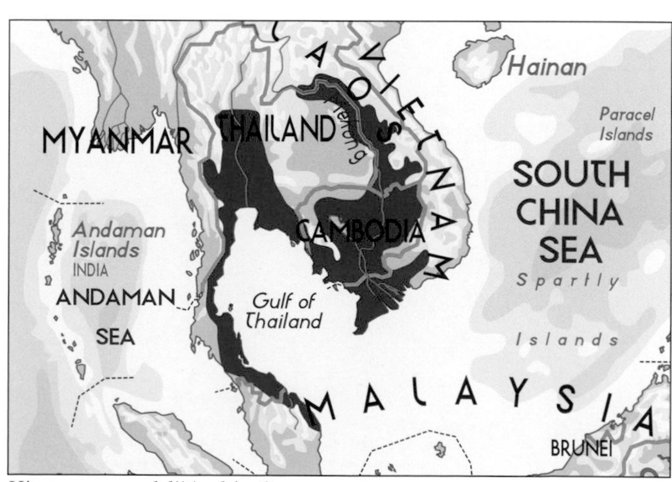

Hieremys annandalii (red/rot)

RT04481-4 *Kachuga dhongoka* (Gray, 1835)

26–48 cm
♀
photo: P.P. van Dijk

RT04482-4 *Kachuga dhongoka* (Gray, 1835)

26–48 cm
♂
photo: P.P. van Dijk

RT04483-4 *Kachuga dhongoka* (Gray, 1835)

26–48 cm
♀
photo: P.P. van Dijk

RT04484-4 *Kachuga dhongoka* (Gray, 1835)

26–48 cm
♂
photo: T. Blanck

RT04485-2 *Kachuga dhongoka* (Gray, 1835)

26–48 cm
Juvenile/Jungtier
photo: P.P. van Dijk

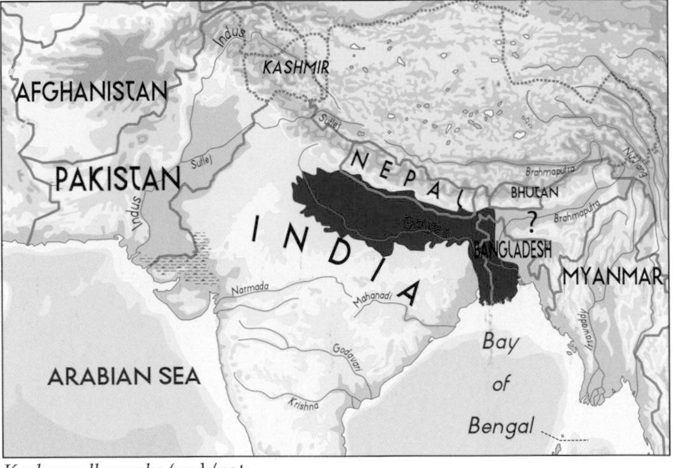

Kachuga dhongoka (red/rot;
?: questionable occurrence/Vorkommen fraglich)

RT04491-4 *Kachuga kachuga* (Gray, 1831)
Chambal River, Madhya Pradesh, India/Indien
35–56 cm
♀ + ♂
photo: P.P. van Dijk

RT04492-4 *Kachuga kachuga* (Gray, 1831)
Chambal River, Madhya Pradesh, India/Indien
35–56 cm
♀
photo: I. Das

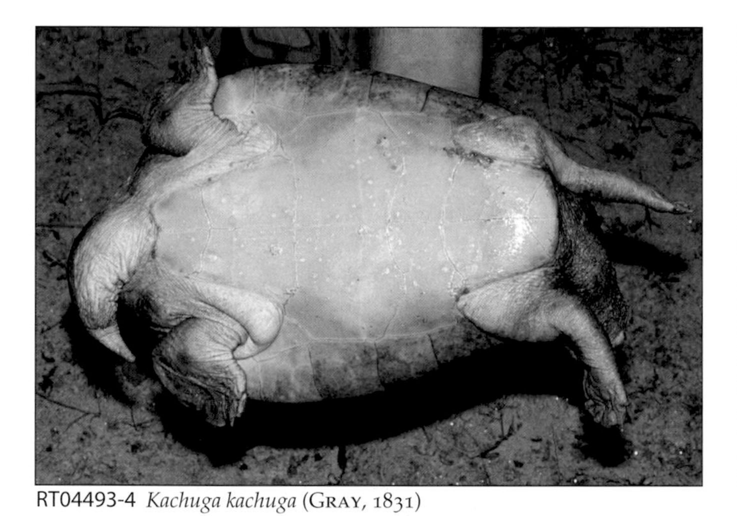

RT04493-4 *Kachuga kachuga* (Gray, 1831)
Chambal River, Madhya Pradesh, India/Indien
35–56 cm
♂
photo: P.P. van Dijk

RT04494-4 *Kachuga kachuga* (Gray, 1831)
Chambal River, Madhya Pradesh, India/Indien
35–56 cm
♂
photo: P.P. van Dijk

RT04495-2 *Kachuga kachuga* (Gray, 1831)
Chambal River, Madhya Pradesh, India/Indien
35–56 cm
Juvenile/Jungtier
photo: P.P. van Dijk

RT04496-4 *Kachuga kachuga* (Gray, 1831)
Chambal River, Madhya Pradesh, India
35–56 cm
♂
photo: I. Das

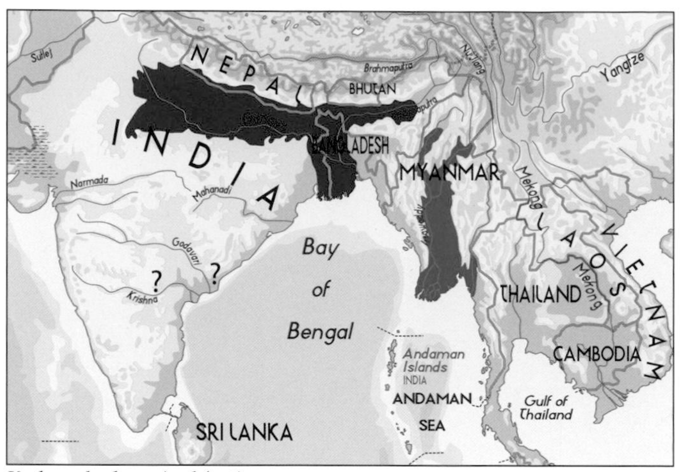

Kachuga kachuga (red / rot)
Kachuga trivittata (blue / blau)

RT04501-4 *Kachuga trivittata* (Duméril & Bibron, 1835)
Myanmar
46–58 cm
♂
photo: B.D. Horne

35°C

RT04502-4 *Kachuga trivittata* (Duméril & Bibron, 1835)
Myanmar
46–58 cm
♀
photo: G. Kuchling

RT04503-4 *Kachuga trivittata* (Duméril & Bibron, 1835)
Myanmar
46–58 cm
♂
photo: G. Kuchling

35°C

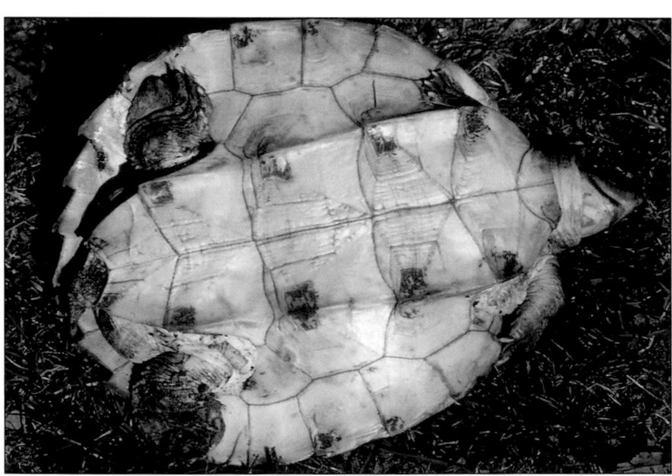

RT04504-2 *Kachuga trivittata* (Duméril & Bibron, 1835)
Myanmar
46–58 cm
Juvenile / Jungtier
photo: W.P. McCord

35°C

RT04505-2 *Kachuga trivittata* (Duméril & Bibron, 1835)
Myanmar
46–58 cm
Juvenile / Jungtier
photo: G. Kuchling

35°C

RT04511-4 *Leucocephalon yuwonoi* (McCord, Iverson & Boeadi, 1995)
Sulawesi, Indonesia/Indonesien
24–26 cm
♂
photo: C. Hagen

RT04512-4 *Leucocephalon yuwonoi* (McCord, Iverson & Boeadi, 1995)
Sulawesi, Indonesia/Indonesien
24–26 cm
♀
photo: C. Hagen

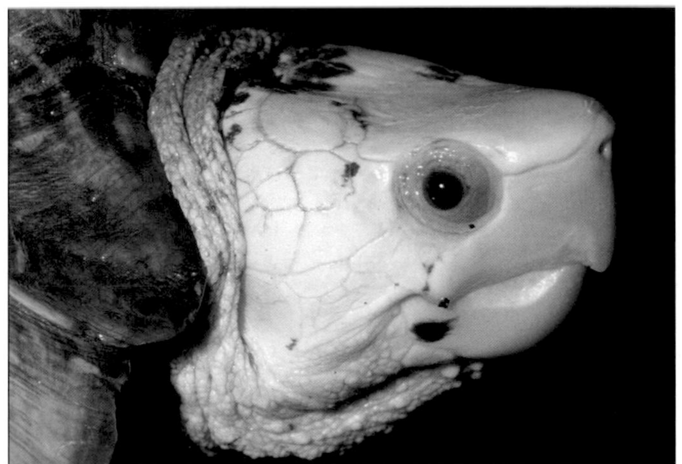

RT04513-4 *Leucocephalon yuwonoi* (McCord, Iverson & Boeadi, 1995)
24–26 cm
♂
photo: J.H. Harding

RT04514-4 *Leucocephalon yuwonoi* (McCord, Iverson & Boeadi, 1995)
Sulawesi, Indonesia/Indonesien
24–26 cm
♂ + ♀
photo: C. Hagen

RT04515-4 *Leucocephalon yuwonoi* (McCord, Iverson & Boeadi, 1995)
International Centre for Conservation of Turtles (Münster, Germany)
24–26 cm
Mating/Paarung
photo: P. Petras

RT04516-1 *Leucocephalon yuwonoi* (McCord, Iverson & Boeadi, 1995)
Sulawesi, Indonesia/Indonesien
24–26 cm
Hatchling/Schlüpfling
photo: C. Hagen

RT04517-4 *Leucocephalon yuwonoi* (McCord, Iverson & Boeadi, 1995)

24–26 cm
♂
photo: J. Maran

RT04518-1 *Leucocephalon yuwonoi* (McCord, Iverson & Boeadi, 1995)
Sulawesi, Indonesia / Indonesien
24–26 cm
Hatchling / Schlüpfling
photo: C. Hagen

Leucocephalon yuwonoi (red / rot)

RT04521-4 *Malayemys macrocephala* (Gray, 1859)
Nakhon Sawan, Thailand
15–21 cm
♂
photo: P.P. van Dijk

RT04522-4 *Malayemys macrocephala* (Gray, 1859)
Bangkok, Thailand
15–21 cm
♂
photo: P.P. van Dijk

RT04523-1 *Malayemys macrocephala* (Gray, 1859)
Bangkok, Thailand
15–21 cm
Hatchling/Schlüpfling
photo: P.P. van Dijk

RT04524-4 *Malayemys macrocephala* (Gray, 1859)
Bangkok, Thailand
15–21 cm
♀
photo: P.P. van Dijk

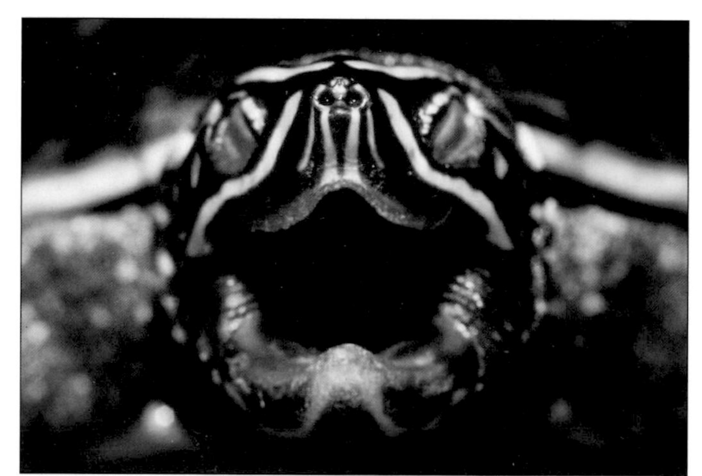

RT04525-4 *Malayemys macrocephala* (Gray, 1859)
SMF 52865 Bangkok, Thailand
15–21 cm
♀
photo: T.R. Brophy

RT04531-4 *Malayemys subtrijuga* (Schlegel & Müller, 1844)

15–21 cm
photo: J.H. Harding

RT04532-4 *Malayemys subtrijuga* (SCHLEGEL & MÜLLER, 1844)

15–21 cm

photo: J. MARAN

RT04533-4 *Malayemys subtrijuga* (SCHLEGEL & MÜLLER, 1844)

15–21 cm

photo: J. MARAN

RT04534-1 *Malayemys subtrijuga* (SCHLEGEL & MÜLLER, 1844)

15–21 cm
Hatchling/Schlüpfling

photo: S. SZYMANSKI

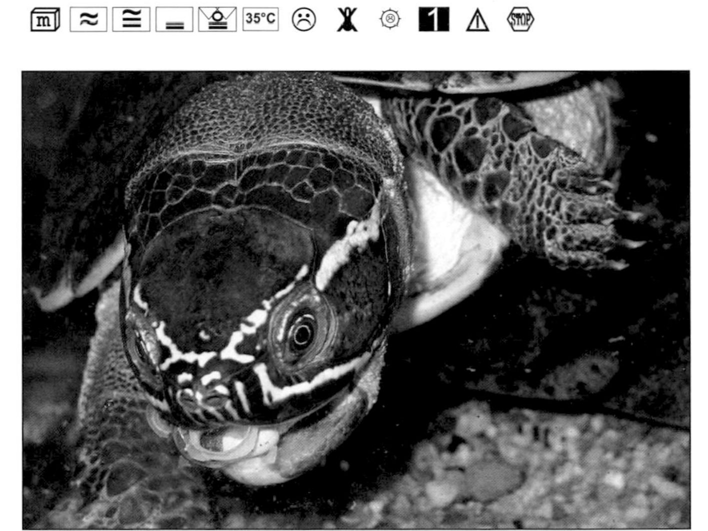

RT04535-4 *Malayemys subtrijuga* (SCHLEGEL & MÜLLER, 1844)

15–21 cm
♂

photo: S. SZYMANSKI

Malayemys macrocephala (red/rot;
?: questionable occurrence/Vorkommen fraglich) – introduced to Sumatra (Indonesia), not depicted here/eingeführt auf Sumatra (Indonesien), hier nicht abgebildet
Malayemys subtrijuga (blue/blau) – introduced to Java and Sumatra (Indonesia), not depicted here/eingeführt auf Java und Sumatra (Indonesien), hier nicht abgebildet

RT04536 *Malayemys subtrijuga* (SCHLEGEL & MÜLLER, 1844)
Habitat, Cambodia/Kambodscha

photo: S. SZYMANSKI

RT04541-4 *Melanochelys tricarinata* (Blyth, 1856)

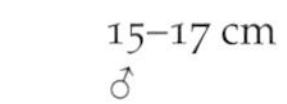

15–17 cm
♂

photo: T. Blanck

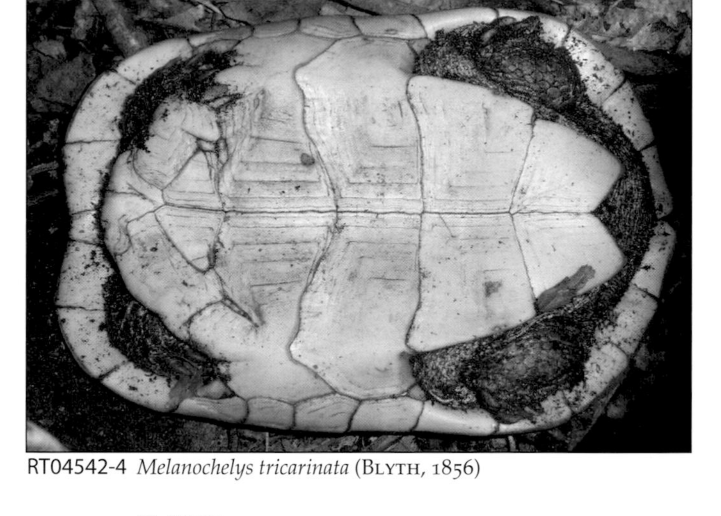

RT04542-4 *Melanochelys tricarinata* (Blyth, 1856)

15–17 cm
♂

photo: T. Blanck

RT04543-4 *Melanochelys tricarinata* (Blyth, 1856)
Bihar, India/Indien
15–17 cm

photo: I. Das

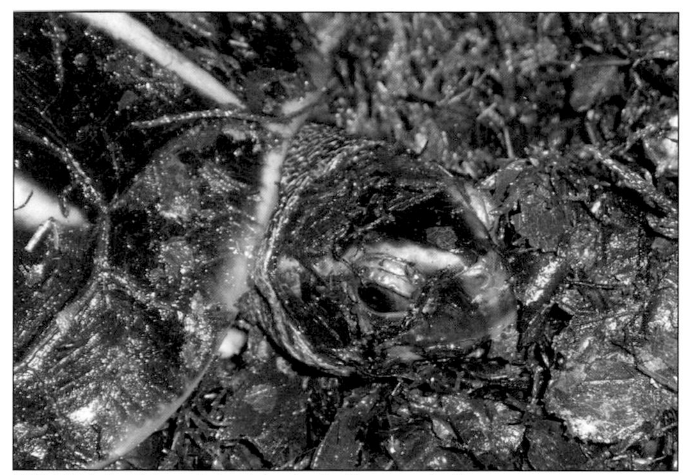

RT04544-4 *Melanochelys tricarinata* (Blyth, 1856)

15–17 cm
♀

photo: T. Blanck

RT04545-2 *Melanochelys tricarinata* (Blyth, 1856)

15–17 cm
Juvenile/Jungtier

photo: P. Praschag

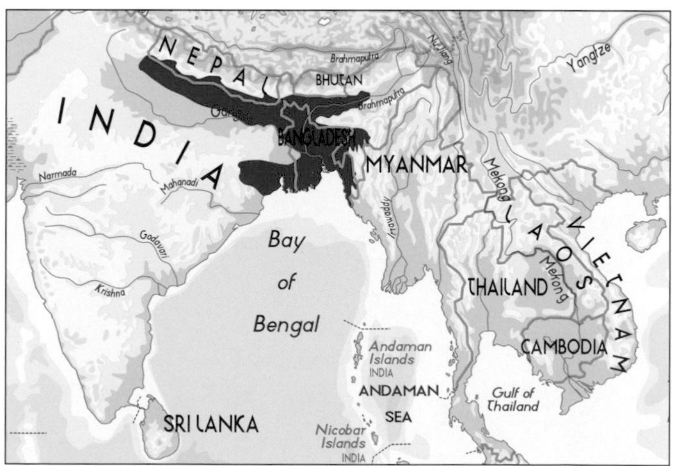

Melanochelys tricarinata (red/rot)

RT04551-4 *Melanochelys trijuga trijuga* (Schweigger, 1812)

20–25 cm

photo: N. Kawazoe/CREEPER

RT04552-4 *Melanochelys trijuga trijuga* (Schweigger, 1812)
Tamil Nadu, India/Indien
20–25 cm
♂

photo: P. Praschag

RT04553-4 *Melanochelys trijuga trijuga* (Schweigger, 1812)

20–25 cm

photo: N. Kawazoe/CREEPER

RT04561-4 *Melanochelys trijuga coronata* (Anderson, 1878)
Kerala, India/Indien
18–21 cm

photo: P. Praschag

RT04562-4 *Melanochelys trijuga coronata* (Anderson, 1878)
Kerala, India/Indien
18–21 cm

photo: I. Das

RT04563-2 *Melanochelys trijuga coronata* (Anderson, 1878)

18–21 cm
Juvenile/Jungtier

photo: J.H. Harding

RT04571-4 *Melanochelys trijuga edeniana* THEOBALD, 1876
Myanmar
25–28 cm
photo: I. DAS

RT04572-4 *Melanochelys trijuga edeniana* THEOBALD, 1876
Myanmar
25–28 cm
photo: I. DAS

RT04573-4 *Melanochelys trijuga edeniana* THEOBALD, 1876
Myanmar
25–28 cm
photo: T. BLANCK

RT04581-4 *Melanochelys trijuga indopeninsularis* (ANNANDALE, 1913)
Chitwan NP, Nepal
30–35 cm
photo: O. BORN

RT04582-4 *Melanochelys trijuga indopeninsularis* (ANNANDALE, 1913)
N W-Bengal, India/Indien
30–35 cm
photo: I. DAS

RT04583-4 *Melanochelys trijuga indopeninsularis* (ANNANDALE, 1913)
Gandak River Area, N Bihar, India/Indien
30–35 cm
Subadult
photo: E.O. MOLL

RT04584-4 *Melanochelys trijuga indopeninsularis* (ANNANDALE, 1913)

30–35 cm

photo: H.-D. PHILIPPEN

RT04591-4 *Melanochelys trijuga parkeri* DERANIYAGALA, 1939

35–39 cm

photo: W.P. MCCORD

RT04592-4 *Melanochelys trijuga parkeri* DERANIYAGALA, 1939
Sri Lanka
35–39 cm

photo: R. SOMAWEERA

RT04593-4 *Melanochelys trijuga parkeri* DERANIYAGALA, 1939
Sri Lanka
35–39 cm

photo: R. SOMAWEERA

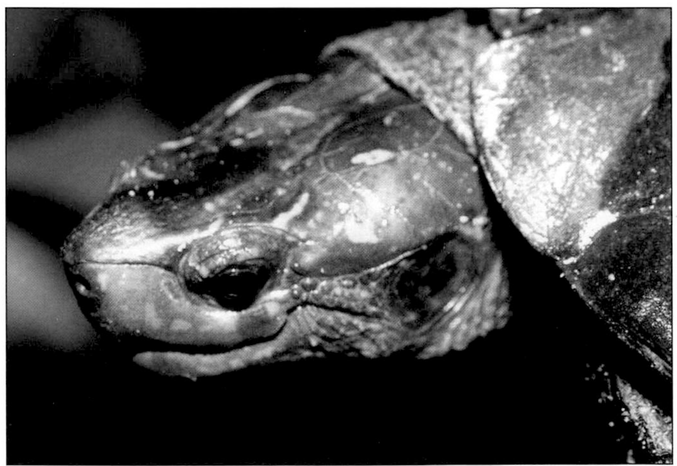

RT04594-4 *Melanochelys trijuga parkeri* DERANIYAGALA, 1939
Sri Lanka
35–39 cm

photo: R. SOMAWEERA

Melanochelys trijuga trijuga (blue/blau); *Melanochelys trijuga coronata* (purple/lila); *Melanochelys trijuga edeniana* (brown/braun); *Melanochelys trijuga indopeninsularis* (green/grün); *Melanochelys trijuga parkeri* (red/rot); *Melanochelys trijuga thermalis* (gray/grau; arrow/Pfeil) – introduced to Chagos Archipelago (British Indian Ocean Territory), not depicted here/ eingeführt auf dem Chagos-Archipel (Britisches Territorium im Indischen Ozean), hier nicht abgebildet; *Melanochelys trijuga wiroti* (orange; arrow/Pfeil), areas of intergradation/Intergradationszonen (pink)

RT04601-4 *Melanochelys trijuga thermalis* (Lesson, 1830)
Sea Turtle Centre, Bentota, Sri Lanka
20–25 cm
♀
photo: P.P. van Dijk

RT04602-4 *Melanochelys trijuga thermalis* (Lesson, 1830)
Sea Turtle Centre, Bentota, Sri Lanka
20–25 cm
♀
photo: P.P. van Dijk

RT04603-4 *Melanochelys trijuga thermalis* (Lesson, 1830)

20–25 cm
photo: J.H. Harding

RT04604-1 *Melanochelys trijuga thermalis* (Lesson, 1830)
Sri Lanka
20–25 cm
Hatchling/Schlüpfling
photo: A. Nöllert

RT04605 *Melanochelys trijuga thermalis* (Lesson, 1830)
Habitat, Sri Lanka
photo: A. Nöllert

RT04611-4 *Melanochelys trijuga wiroti* (Reimann, 1979)
Pata Zoo, Bangkok, Thailand
25–28 cm
photo: P.P. van Dijk

RT04621-4 *Morenia ocellata* (DUMÉRIL & BIBRON, 1835)
Myanmar
15–22 cm
photo: I. DAS

RT04622-2 *Morenia ocellata* (DUMÉRIL & BIBRON, 1835)
Myanmar
15–22 cm
Juvenile/Jungtier
photo: P.P. VAN DIJK

RT04623-4 *Morenia ocellata* (DUMÉRIL & BIBRON, 1835)

15–22 cm
photo: H.-D. PHILIPPEN

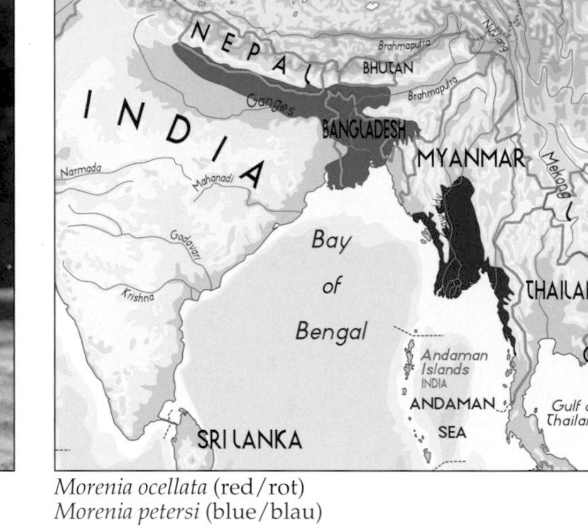

Morenia ocellata (red/rot)
Morenia petersi (blue/blau)

RT04631-4 *Morenia petersi* (ANDERSON, 1879)

15–20 cm
photo: M. ROGNER

RT04632-4 *Morenia petersi* (ANDERSON, 1879)

15–20 cm
♂
photo: B. WOLFF

RT04633-4 *Morenia petersi* (Anderson, 1879)
Bangladesh/Bangladesch
15–20 cm

photo: I. Das

RT04634-4 *Morenia petersi* (Anderson, 1879)
Sunargon, Bangladesh/Bangladesch
15–20 cm

photo: P. Praschag

RT04635-5 *Morenia petersi* (Anderson, 1879)

15–20 cm
♀

photo: P.P. van Dijk

RT04636-5 *Morenia petersi* (Anderson, 1879)

15–20 cm
♀

photo: P.P. van Dijk

RT04637-2 *Morenia petersi* (Anderson, 1879)

15–20 cm
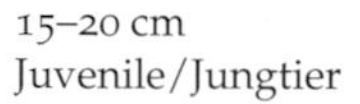
Juvenile/Jungtier

photo: N. Kawazoe/CREEPER

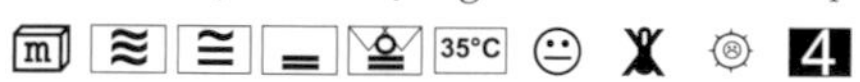

RT04638-3 *Morenia petersi* (Anderson, 1879)

15–20 cm
Subadult

photo: N. Kawazoe/CREEPER

RT04641-4 *Notochelys platynota* (Gray, 1834)
Loagan Bunut, Sarawak, Malaysia
30–32 cm
photo: I. Das

RT04642-4 *Notochelys platynota* (Gray, 1834)
30–32 cm
♀ + ♂
photo: P.P. van Dijk

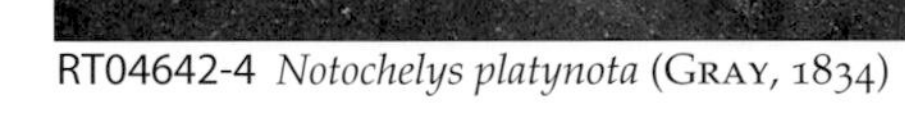

RT04643-4 *Notochelys platynota* (Gray, 1834)
30–32 cm
photo: J.H. Harding

RT04644-2 *Notochelys platynota* (Gray, 1834)
30–32 cm
Juvenile/Jungtier
photo: J.H. Harding

RT04645-1 *Notochelys platynota* (Gray, 1834)
30–32 cm
Hatchling/Schlüpfling
photo: P.P. van Dijk

Notochelys platynota (red/rot;
?: questionable occurrence/Vorkommen fraglich)

RT04651-4 *Ocadia japonica* (Temminck & Schlegel, 1835)

15–19 cm
♀
photo: J. Maran

RT04652-4 *Ocadia japonica* (Temminck & Schlegel, 1835)
Soshiki River, Kyushu, Japan
15–19 cm
♀
photo: P. Petras

RT04653-4 *Ocadia japonica* (Temminck & Schlegel, 1835)

15–19 cm
♀
photo: U. Jost

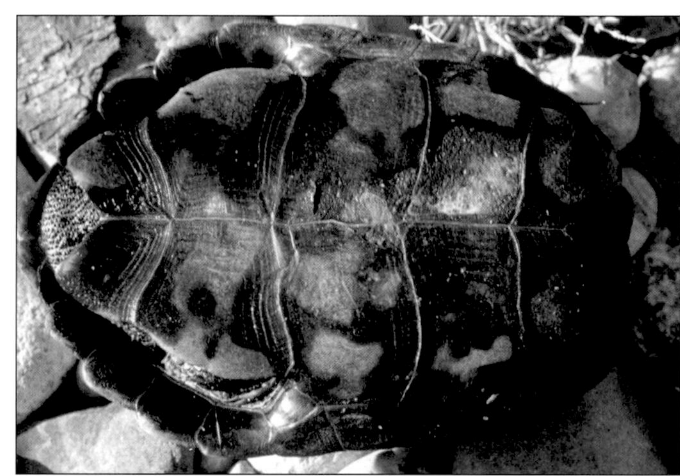

RT04654-4 *Ocadia japonica* (Temminck & Schlegel, 1835)

15–19 cm
♀
photo: U. Jost

RT04655-4 *Ocadia japonica* (Temminck & Schlegel, 1835)

15–19 cm
photo: T. Blanck

RT04656-4 *Ocadia japonica* (Temminck & Schlegel, 1835)

15–19 cm
photo: F. Wüthrich

RT04657-4 *Ocadia japonica* (TEMMINCK & SCHLEGEL, 1835)

15–19 cm
Oviposition/Eiablage

photo: U. JOST

RT04658-1 *Ocadia japonica* (TEMMINCK & SCHLEGEL, 1835)

15–19 cm
Hatchling/Schlüpfling

photo: U. JOST

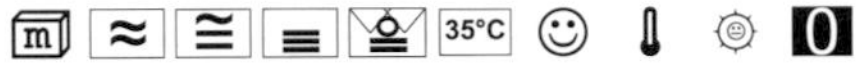

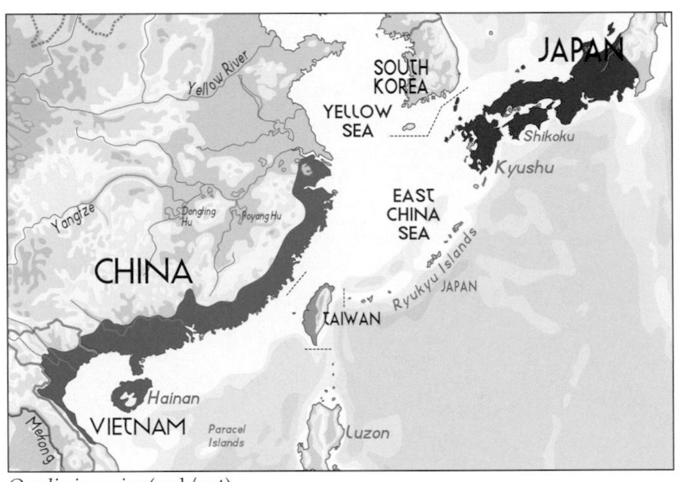

Ocadia japonica (red/rot)
Ocadia sinensis "Chinese form/Chinesische Form" (blue/blau)
Ocadia sinensis "Taiwan form/Taiwan-Form" (orange)

RT04661 *Ocadia sinensis* (GRAY, 1834)
"Chinese form/Chinesische Form"
Habitat, Lamma Island, China

photo: T. BLANCK

RT04662-4 *Ocadia sinensis* (GRAY, 1834)
"Chinese form/Chinesische Form"
20–30 cm
♂

photo: J. B IVERSON

RT04663-4 *Ocadia sinensis* (GRAY, 1834)
"Chinese form/Chinesische Form"
20–30 cm

photo: M. SCHILDE

RT04664-4 *Ocadia sinensis* (GRAY, 1834)
"Chinese form/Chinesische Form"
20–30 cm

photo: M. SCHILDE

RT04665-4 *Ocadia sinensis* (GRAY, 1834)
"Chinese form/Chinesische Form"
20–30 cm
♂

photo: J. MARAN

RT04666-4 *Ocadia sinensis* (GRAY, 1834)
"Chinese form/Chinesische Form"
20–30 cm

photo: M. SCHILDE

RT04671-4 *Ocadia sinensis* (GRAY, 1834)
"Taiwan form/Taiwan–Form"
20–30 cm

photo: I. DAS

RT04672-4 *Ocadia sinensis* (GRAY, 1834)
"Taiwan form/Taiwan–Form"
20–30 cm

photo: P.P. VAN DIJK

RT04673-4 *Ocadia sinensis* (GRAY, 1834)
"Taiwan form/Taiwan–Form"
20–30 cm

photo: M. SCHILDE

RT04681-4 *Orlitia borneensis* GRAY, 1873

70–80 cm
♂
photo: J. MARAN

RT04682-4 *Orlitia borneensis* GRAY, 1873

70–80 cm
♂
photo: J. MARAN

RT04683-4 *Orlitia borneensis* GRAY, 1873

70–80 cm
♂
photo: J. MARAN

RT04684-4 *Orlitia borneensis* GRAY, 1873

70–80 cm
♂
photo: S. SZYMANSKI

RT04685-4 *Orlitia borneensis* GRAY, 1873

70–80 cm
photo: J. VOGELTANZ

Orlitia borneensis (red/rot)

RT04691-4 *Panayaenemys leytensis* (TAYLOR, 1920)
Palawan, Phlippines/Philippinen
20–21 cm

photo: P. FIDENCI

RT04692-4 *Panayaenemys leytensis* (TAYLOR, 1920)
Palawan, Phlippines/Philippinen
20–21 cm

photo: P. FIDENCI

RT04693-4 *Panayaenemys leytensis* (TAYLOR, 1920)
Palawan, Phlippines/Philippinen
20–21 cm

photo: I. DAS

RT04694-4 *Panayaenemys leytensis* (TAYLOR, 1920)
Palawan, Phlippines/Philippinen
20–21 cm

photo: I. DAS

RT04695-4 *Panayaenemys leytensis* (TAYLOR, 1920)
Palawan, Phlippines/Philippinen
20–21 cm

photo: P. FIDENCI

Panayaenemys leytensis (red/rot;
?: questionable occurrence/Vorkommen fraglich)

RT04701-4 *Pangshura flaviventer* GÜNTHER, 1864

15–22 cm

photo: P.P. VAN DIJK

RT04702-4 *Pangshura flaviventer* GÜNTHER, 1864
Sunargon, Bangladhesh/Bangladhesch
15–22 cm
♀+ ♂

photo: P. PRASCHAG

RT04703-4 *Pangshura flaviventer* GÜNTHER, 1864

15–22 cm
♀

photo: T. BLANCK

RT04704-4 *Pangshura flaviventer* GÜNTHER, 1864
Sunargon, Bangladhesh/Bangladhesch
15–22 cm
♀

photo: P. PRASCHAG

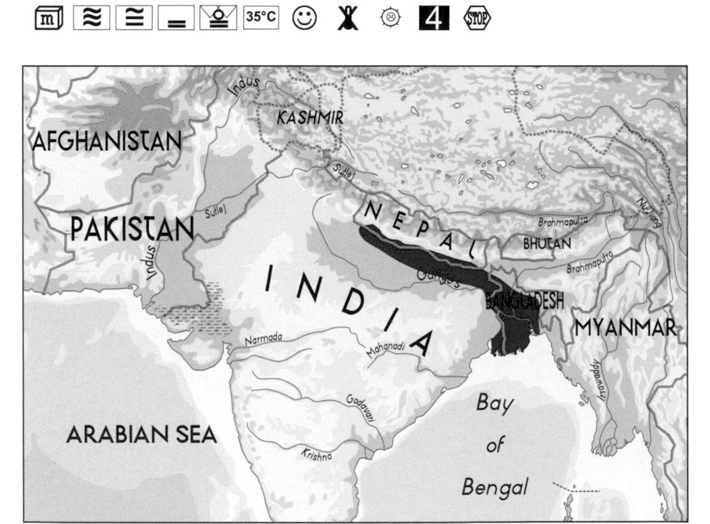

Pangshura flaviventer (red/rot)

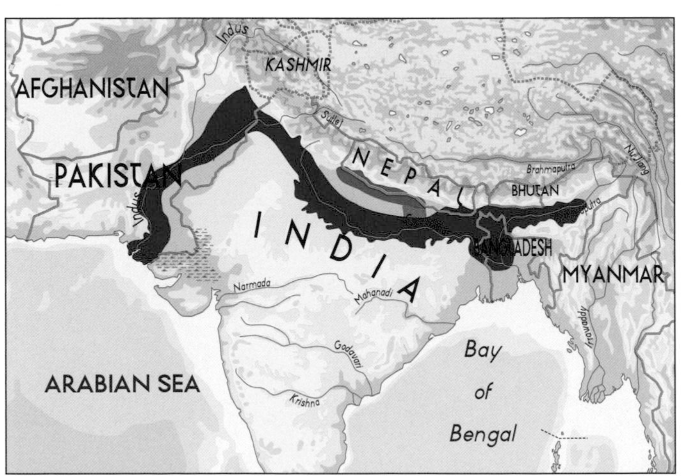

Pangshura smithii smithii (red/rot),
Pangshura smithii pallidipes (blue/blau)
areas of intergradation/Intergradationszonen (pink)

RT04711-4 *Pangshura smithii smithii* (GRAY, 1863)
Chambal River, Madhya Pradesh, India/Indien
20–24 cm
photo: I. DAS

RT04712-4 *Pangshura smithii smithii* (GRAY, 1863)
Brahmaputra, Assam, India/Indien
20–24 cm
♀
photo: P. PRASCHAG

RT04713-4 *Pangshura smithii smithii* (GRAY, 1863)
Brahmaputra, Assam, India/Indien
20–24 cm
♀
photo: P. PRASCHAG

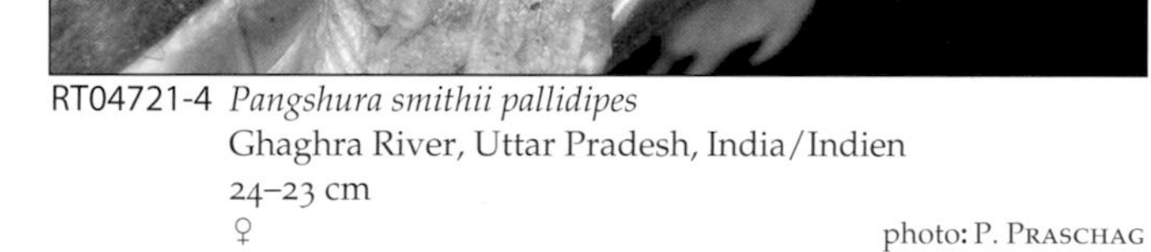

RT04721-4 *Pangshura smithii pallidipes*
Ghaghra River, Uttar Pradesh, India/Indien
24–23 cm
♀
photo: P. PRASCHAG

RT04722-4 *Pangshura smithii pallidipes*
India/Indien
24–23 cm
photo: I. DAS

RT04723-4 *Pangshura smithii pallidipes*
Ghaghra River, Uttar Pradesh, India/Indien
24–23 cm
♂
photo: P. PRASCHAG

RT04731-4 *Pangshura sylhetensis* Jerdon, 1870

18–20 cm

photo: N. Kawazoe/CREEPER

RT04732-4 *Pangshura sylhetensis* Jerdon, 1870

18–20 cm

photo: N. Kawazoe/CREEPER

RT04733-4 *Pangshura sylhetensis* Jerdon, 1870
Nameri NP, Assam, India/Indien
18–20 cm
♀

photo: P. Praschag

RT04734-2 *Pangshura sylhetensis* Jerdon, 1870
Nameri NP, Assam, India/Indien
18–20 cm
Juvenile/Jungtier

photo: P. Praschag

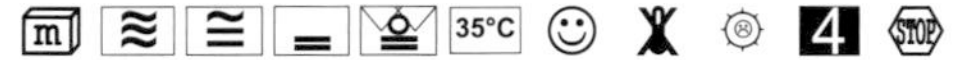

RT04735 *Pangshura sylhetensis* Jerdon, 1870
Kaziranga NP, Assam, India/Indien

photo: P. Praschag

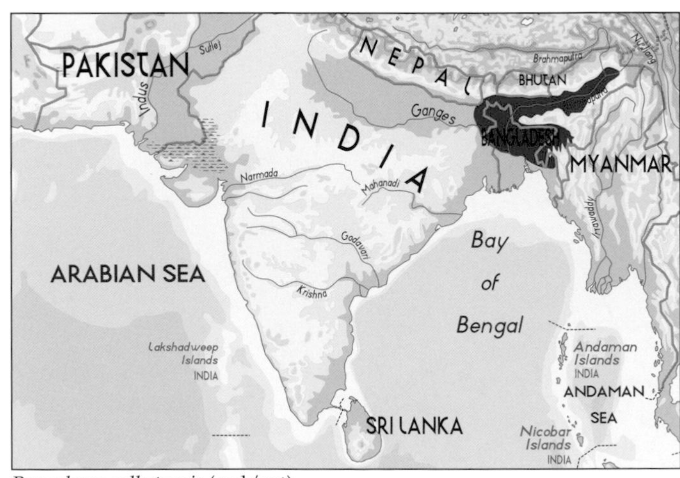

Pangshura sylhetensis (red/rot)

RT04741-4 *Pangshura tectum* (Gray, 1831)

15–23 cm

photo: P.P. van Dijk

RT04741-4 *Pangshura tectum* (Gray, 1831)
Dhaka, Bangladesh / Bangladesch
15–23 cm
♂ + ♀

photo: P. Praschag

RT04743-4 *Pangshura tectum* (Gray, 1831)

15–23 cm
♂

photo: T. Berndt/A. Mende

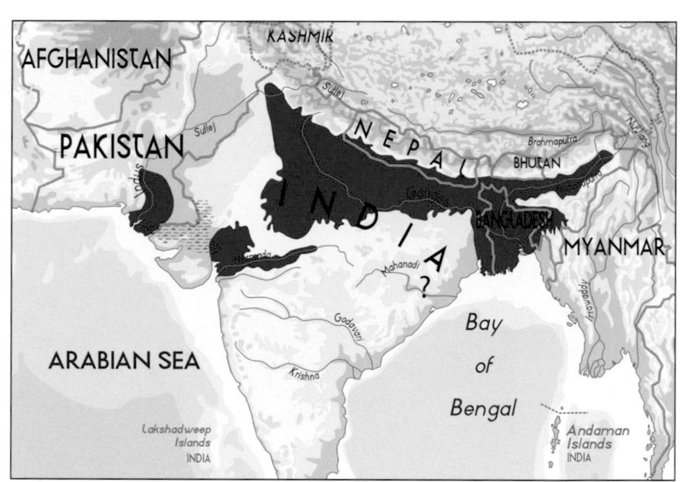

Pangshura tectum (red/rot)
?: (questionable occurrence/Vorkommen fraglich)

RT04744-3 *Pangshura tectum* (Gray, 1831)
India/Indien
15–23 cm
Subadult

photo: I. Das

RT04745-1 *Pangshura tectum* (Gray, 1831)
India/Indien
15–23 cm
Hatchling/Schlüpfling

photo: M. Rogner

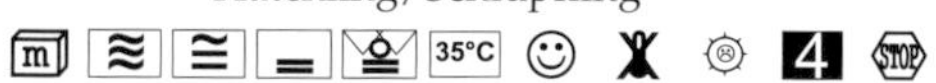

RT04746-4 *Pangshura tectum* (GRAY, 1831)
India/Indien
15–23 cm

photo: B. WOLFF

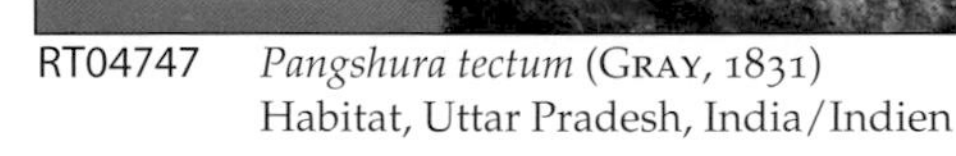

RT04747 *Pangshura tectum* (GRAY, 1831)
Habitat, Uttar Pradesh, India/Indien

photo: P.P. VAN DIJK

RT04751-4 *Pangshura tentoria tentoria* (GRAY, 1834)

18–23 cm

photo: P.P. VAN DIJK

RT04752-4 *Pangshura tentoria tentoria* (GRAY, 1834)

18–23 cm

photo: P.P. VAN DIJK

RT04753-4 *Pangshura tentoria tentoria* (GRAY, 1834)

18–23 cm

photo: I. DAS

Pangshura tentoria tentoria (red/rot)
Pangshura tentoria circumdata (blue/blau)
Pangshura tentoria "Brahmaputra form/Brahmaputra-Form" (orange)
?: questionable occurrence/Vorkommen fraglich

RT04761-4 *Pangshura tentoria circumdata* (Mertens, 1969)
Ghaghra River, Uttar Pradesh, India / Indien
18–27 cm
♂
photo: P. Praschag

RT04762-4 *Pangshura tentoria circumdata* (Mertens, 1969)

18–27 cm

photo: P.P. van Dijk

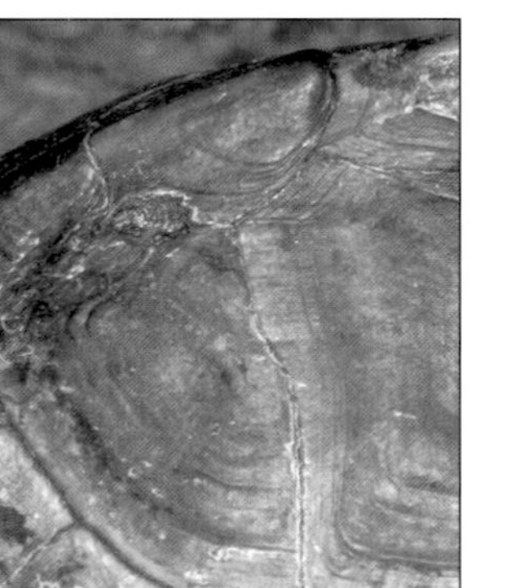

RT04763-4 *Pangshura tentoria circumdata* (Mertens, 1969)

18–27 cm

photo: I. Das

RT04764 *Pangshura tentoria circumdata* (Mertens, 1969)
Habitat, Chambal River, Madhya Pradesh, India / Indien

photo: P.P. van Dijk

RT04771-4 *Pangshura tentoria* "Brahmaputra form / Brahmaputra–Form"
Brahmaputra, Assam, India
18–27 cm
♀
photo: P. Praschag

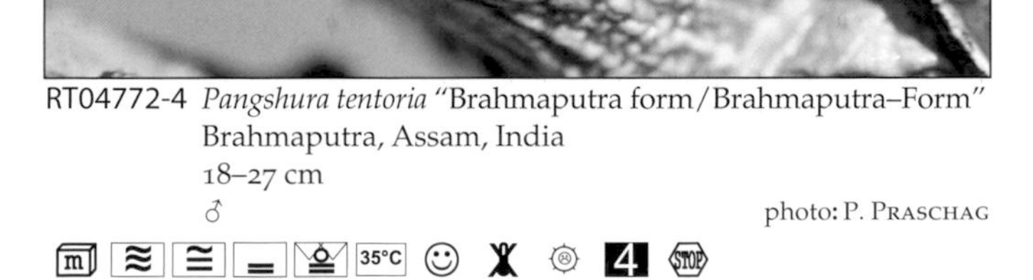

RT04772-4 *Pangshura tentoria* "Brahmaputra form / Brahmaputra–Form"
Brahmaputra, Assam, India
18–27 cm
♂
photo: P. Praschag

RT04781-4 *Pyxiclemmys pani pani* (Song, 1984)

13–20 cm

photo: J. Maran/R. Amann

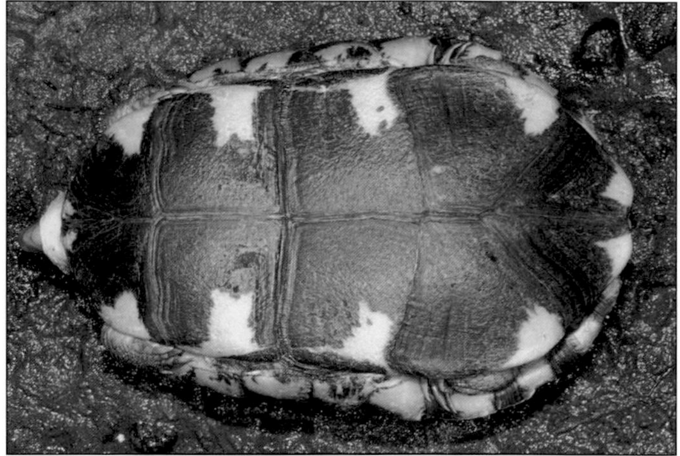

RT04782-4 *Pyxiclemmys pani pani* (Song, 1984)

13–20 cm
♀

photo: A. Nöllert

RT04783-4 *Pyxiclemmys pani pani* (Song, 1984)

13–17 cm
♀

photo: T. Blanck

RT04791-4 *Pyxiclemmys pani aurocapitata* (Luo & Zong, 1988)
intermediate form/intermediäre Form
12–16 cm

photo: T. Blanck

RT04792-4 *Pyxiclemmys pani aurocapitata* (Luo & Zong, 1988)

12–16 cm

photo: T. Blanck

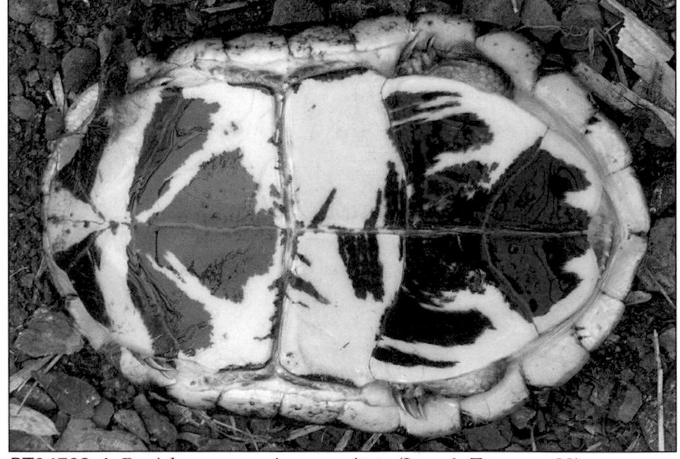

RT04793-4 *Pyxiclemmys pani aurocapitata* (Luo & Zong, 1988)

12–16 cm
♂

photo: T. Blanck

RT04794-4 *Pyxiclemmys pani aurocapitata* (Luo & Zong, 1988)

12–16 cm
♀

photo: T. Blanck

RT04795-4 *Pyxiclemmys pani aurocapitata* (Luo & Zong, 1988)

12–16 cm
♀

photo: T. Blanck

RT04796-4 *Pyxiclemmys pani aurocapitata* (Luo & Zong, 1988)

12–16 cm
♀

photo: J.B. Iverson

RT04797-4 *Pyxiclemmys pani aurocapitata* (Luo & Zong, 1988)

12–16 cm
♂

photo: J.B. Iverson

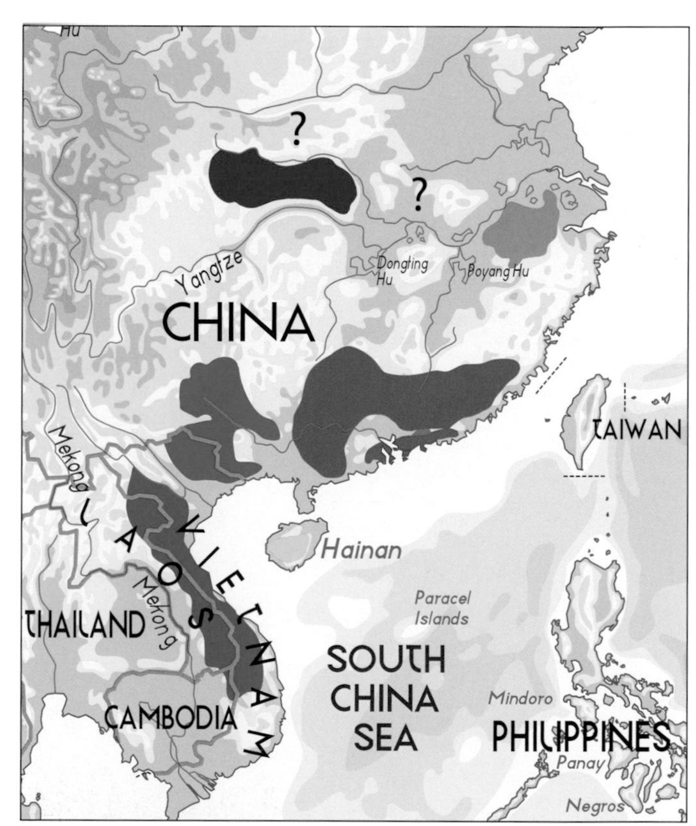

Pyxiclemmys pani pani (red/rot;
?: questionable occurrence/Vorkommen fraglich)
Pyxiclemmys pani aurocapitata (orange)
Pyxiclemmys trifasciata "Annam form/Annam-Form" (blue/blau)
Pyxiclemmys trifasciata "Guangdong form/Guangdong-Form" (brown/braun)
Pyxiclemmys trifasciata "Hainan form/Hainan-Form" (yellow/gelb)
Pyxiclemmys trifasciata "Hong Kong form/Hongkong-Form" (purple/lila)
Pyxiclemmys trifasciata "Northern Vietnamese form/Nordvietnamesische Form" (green/grün)
area of intergradation/Intergradationszone (pink)

RT04801-4 *Pyxiclemmys trifasciata* (Bell, 1825)
"Annam form/Annam-Form"
23–27 cm
♀
photo: T. Blanck

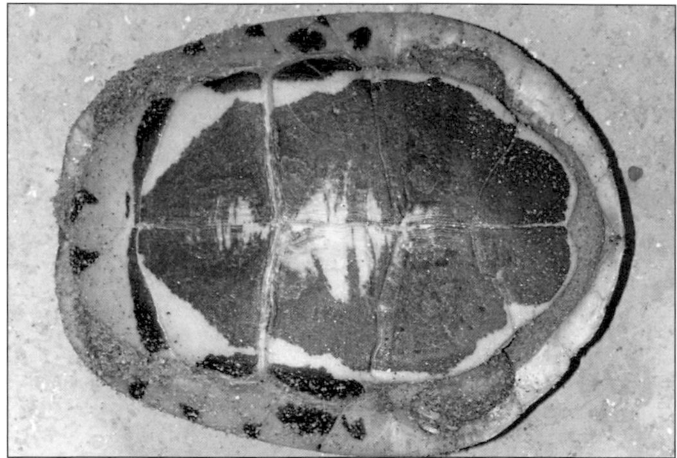

RT04802-4 *Pyxiclemmys trifasciata* (Bell, 1825)
"Annam form/Annam-Form"
23–27 cm
♂
photo: T. Blanck

RT04811-4 *Pyxiclemmys trifasciata* (Bell, 1825)
"Guangdong form/Guangdong-Form"
18–23 cm
♂
photo: P.P. van Dijk

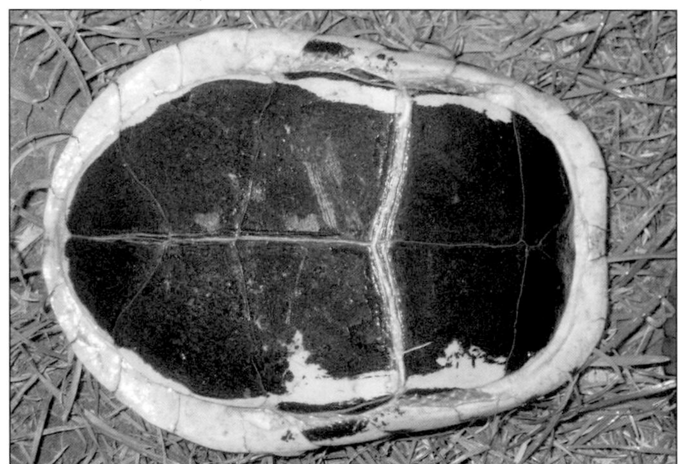

RT04812-4 *Pyxiclemmys trifasciata* (Bell, 1825)
"Guangdong form/Guangdong-Form"
18–23 cm
♀
photo: T. Blanck

RT04813-4 *Pyxiclemmys trifasciata* (Bell, 1825)
"Guangdong form/Guangdong-Form"
18–23 cm
♂
photo: P.P. van Dijk

RT04814-2 *Pyxiclemmys trifasciata* (Bell, 1825)
"Guangdong form/Guangdong-Form"
18–23 cm
Juvenile/Jungtier
photo: P.P. van Dijk

RT04821-4 *Pyxiclemmys trifasciata* (BELL, 1825)
"Hainan form/Hainan–Form"
17–21 cm
♂

photo: J.H. HARDING

RT04822-4 *Pyxiclemmys trifasciata* (BELL, 1825)
"Hainan form/Hainan–Form"
17–21 cm
♂

photo: J.H. HARDING

RT04831-4 *Pyxiclemmys trifasciata* (BELL, 1825)
"Hong Kong form/Hongkong–Form"
16–18 cm

photo: S. SEKI

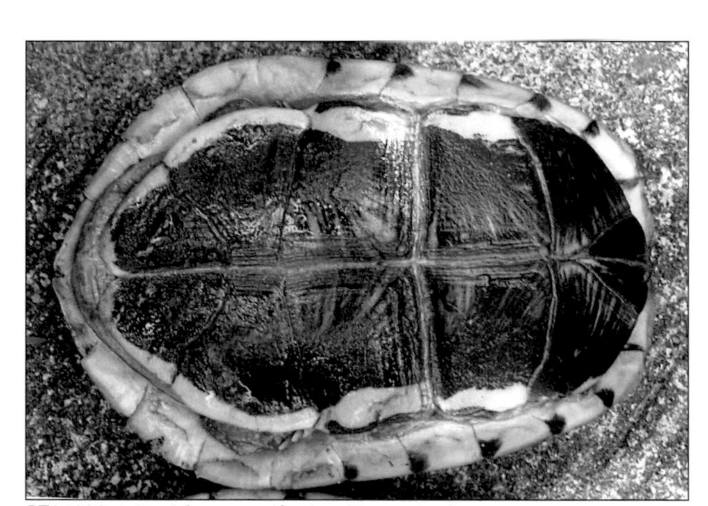

RT04832-4 *Pyxiclemmys trifasciata* (BELL, 1825)
"Hong Kong form/Hongkong–Form"
16–18 cm

photo: T. BLANCK

RT04841-4 *Pyxiclemmys trifasciata* (BELL, 1825) "Northern Vietnamese form/Nordvietnamesische Form"
24–30 cm

photo: J.B. IVERSON

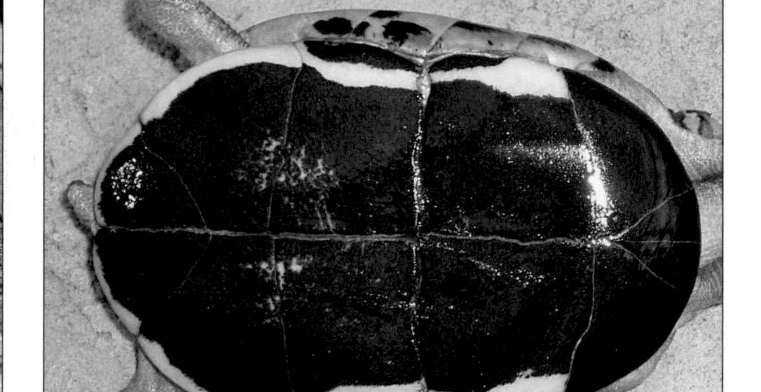

RT04842-4 *Pyxiclemmys trifasciata* (BELL, 1825) "Northern Vietnamese form/Nordvietnamesische Form"
24–30 cm
♂

photo: T. BLANCK

RT04851-4 *Pyxiclemmys yunnanensis* (Boulenger, 1906)

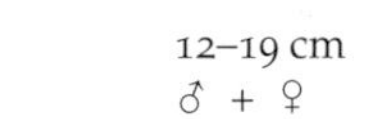

12–19 cm
♂ + ♀
photo: Zhou Ting/T. Blanck

RT04852-4 *Pyxiclemmys yunnanensis* (Boulenger, 1906)

12–19 cm
♂ + ♀
photo: Zhou Ting/T. Blanck

RT04853-4 *Pyxiclemmys yunnanensis* (Boulenger, 1906)

12–19 cm
♂
photo: Zhou Ting/T. Blanck

RT04854-4 *Pyxiclemmys yunnanensis* (Boulenger, 1906)

12–19 cm
♀
photo: Zhou Ting/T. Blanck

RT04855-4 *Pyxiclemmys yunnanensis* (Boulenger, 1906)

12–19 cm
♂
photo: Zhou Ting/T. Blanck

Pyxiclemmys yunnanensis (red/rot)
Pyxiclemmys zhoui (blue/blau)

RT04861-4 *Pyxiclemmys zhoui* (Zhao, 1990)

16–19 cm
♀

photo: T. Blanck

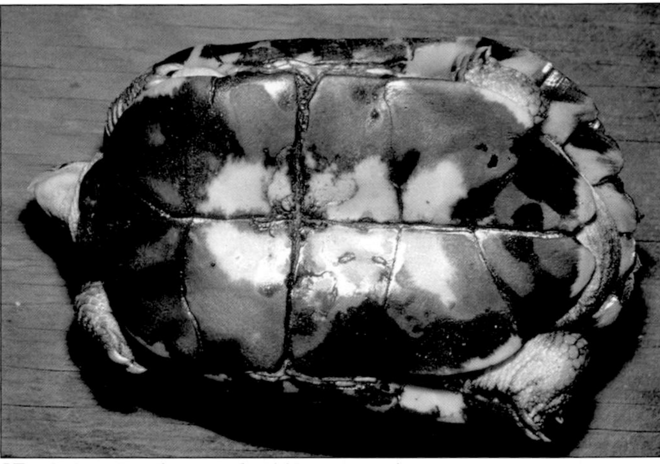

RT04862-4 *Pyxiclemmys zhoui* (Zhao, 1990)

16–19 cm
♂

photo: J. B. Iverson

RT04863-4 *Pyxiclemmys zhoui* (Zhao, 1990)

16–19 cm
♀

photo: T. Blanck

RT04864-4 *Pyxiclemmys zhoui* (Zhao, 1990)

16–19 cm
♂

photo: J. B. Iverson

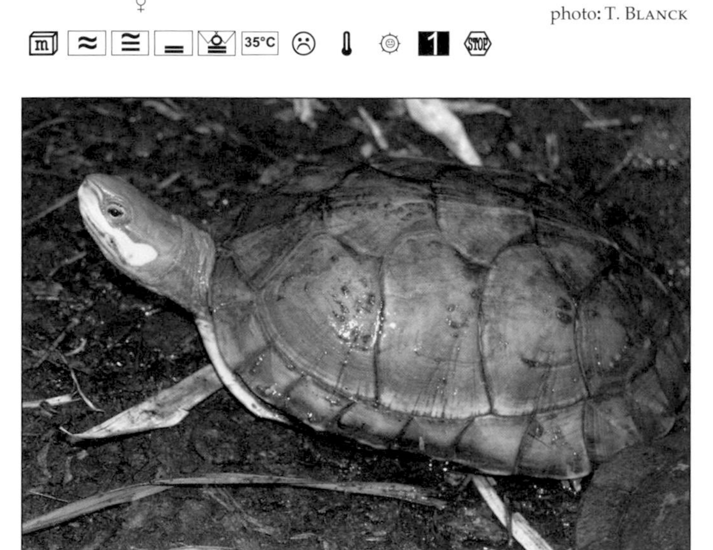

RT04865-4 *Pyxiclemmys zhoui* (Zhao, 1990)

16–19 cm
♀

photo: T. Blanck

RT04866-2 *Pyxiclemmys zhoui* (Zhao, 1990)

16–19 cm
Juvenile/Jungtier

photo: T. Blanck

RT04871-4 *Pyxidea mouhotii mouhotii* (GRAY, 1862)
Laos
18–21 cm
photo: P.P. VAN DIJK

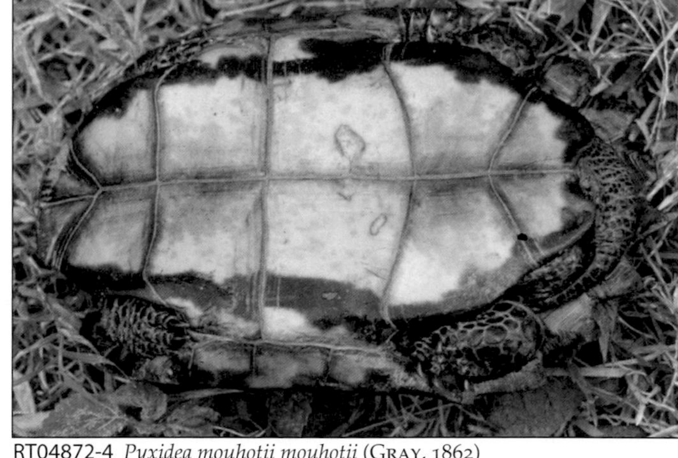

RT04872-4 *Pyxidea mouhotii mouhotii* (GRAY, 1862)
18–21 cm
photo: M. SCHILDE

RT04873-2 *Pyxidea mouhotii mouhotii* (GRAY, 1862)
18–21 cm
Juvenile/Jungtier
photo: S. PAWLOWSKI

RT04874-4 *Pyxidea mouhotii mouhotii* (GRAY, 1862)
18–21 cm
photo: T. BLANCK

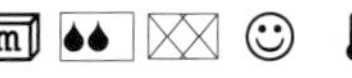

Pyxidea mouhotii mouhotii (red/rot)
Pyxidea mouhotii obsti (blue/blau)
Pyxidea mouhotii "Indian form/Indische Form" (orange)
areas of intergradation/Intergradationszonen (pink)
?: questionable occurrence/Vorkommen fraglich

RT04882-4 *Pyxidea mouhotii obsti* FRITZ, ANDREAS & LEHR, 1998
15–18 cm
♀
photo: S. PAWLOWSKI

RT04882-4 *Pyxidea mouhotii obsti* Fritz, Andreas & Lehr, 1998

15–18 cm
♀
photo: T. Berndt/A. Mende

RT04883-4 *Pyxidea mouhotii obsti* Fritz, Andreas & Lehr, 1998

15–18 cm
♂
photo: T. Blanck

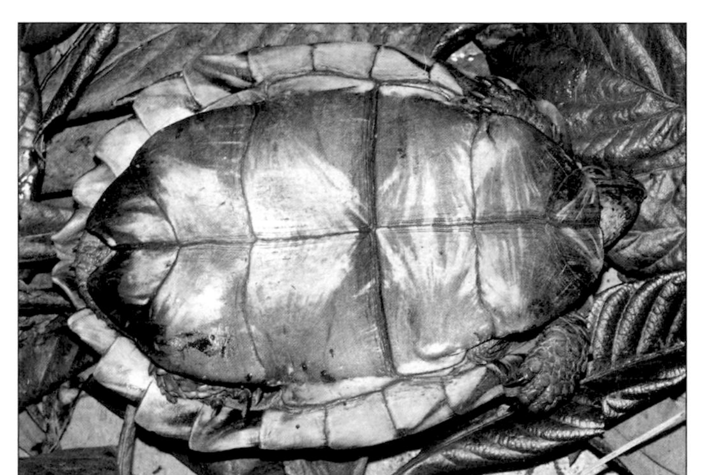

RT04891-4 *Pyxidea mouhotii obsti* Fritz, Andreas & Lehr, 1998

15–18 cm
photo: T. Blanck

RT04892-4 *Pyxidea mouhotii* "Indian form/Indische Form"

15–18 cm
photo: T. Blanck

RT04893-4 *Pyxidea mouhotii* "Indian form/Indische Form"

15–18 cm
photo: T. Blanck

       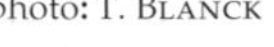

RT04894-4 *Pyxidea mouhotii* "Indian form/Indische Form"
Myanmar
15–18 cm
photo: T. Blanck

RT04901-4 *Sacalia bealei* (Gray, 1831)

12–15 cm

photo: T. Berndt/A. Mende

RT04902-4 *Sacalia bealei* (Gray, 1831)

12–15 cm
♀

photo: J.B. Iverson

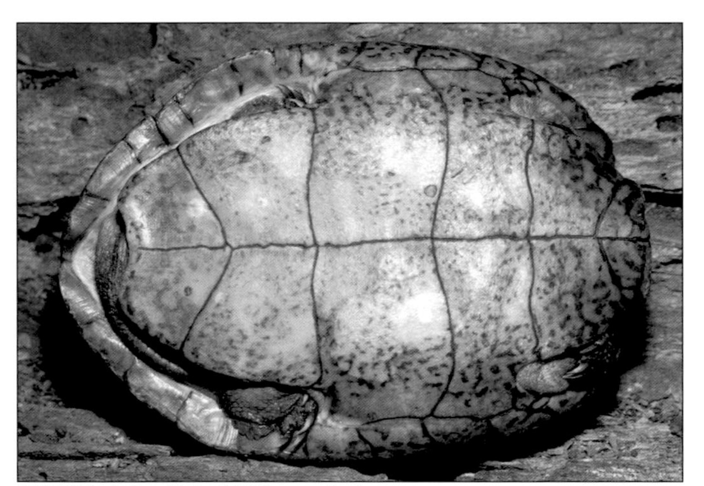

RT04903-4 *Sacalia bealei* (Gray, 1831)

12–15 cm
♂

photo: J.B. Iverson

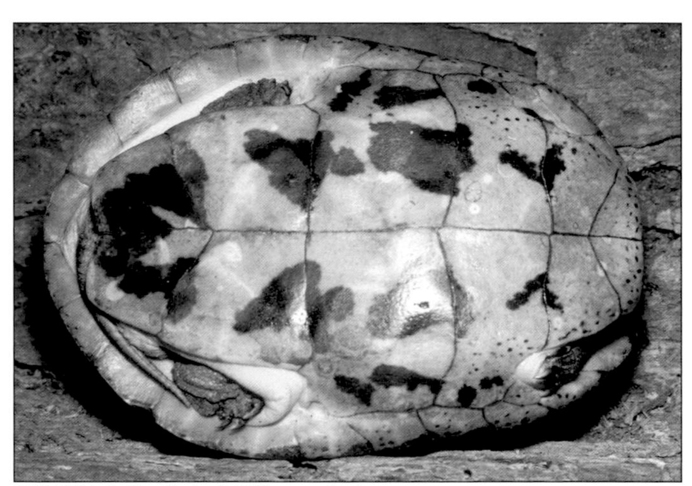

RT04904-4 *Sacalia bealei* (Gray, 1831)

12–15 cm
♀

photo: J.B. Iverson

RT04905-4 *Sacalia bealei* (Gray, 1831)

12–15 cm
♂

photo: T. Blanck

RT04906-4 *Sacalia bealei* (Gray, 1831)

12–15 cm
♀

photo: T. Blanck

RT04907-4 *Sacalia bealei* (Gray, 1831)

12–15 cm

photo: J.H. Harding

RT04908-2 *Sacalia bealei* (Gray, 1831)

12–15 cm
Juvenile/Jungtier

photo: M. Rogner

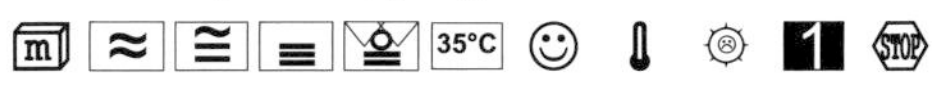

Sacalia bealei (red/rot)

Sacalia quadriocellata "Hainan form/Hainan-Form" (red/rot)
Sacalia quadriocellata "Mainland form/Festland-Form" (blue/blau)

RT04911-4 *Sacalia quadriocellata* (Siebenrock, 1903)
"Hainan form/Hainan–Form"
15–18 cm
♀

photo: T. Blanck

RT04911-4 *Sacalia quadriocellata* (Siebenrock, 1903)
"Hainan form/Hainan–Form"
15–18 cm
♀ + ♂

photo: T. Blanck

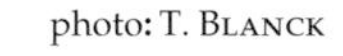

RT04913-4 *Sacalia quadriocellata* (SIEBENROCK, 1903)
"Hainan form/Hainan-Form"
15–18 cm
♂
photo: P.P. VAN DIJK

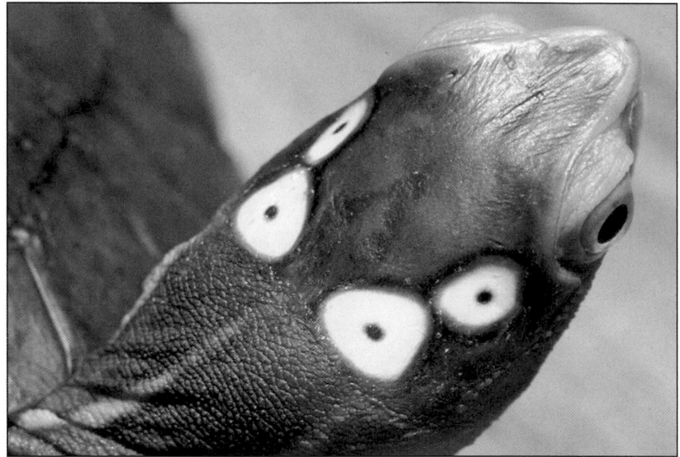

RT04914-2 *Sacalia quadriocellata* (SIEBENROCK, 1903)
"Hainan form/Hainan-Form"
15–18 cm
♀
photo: P.P. VAN DIJK

RT04915-4 *Sacalia quadriocellata* (SIEBENROCK, 1903)
"Hainan form/Hainan-Form"
Habitat, Hainan, China
photo: P.P. VAN DIJK

RT04916-2 *Sacalia quadriocellata* (SIEBENROCK, 1903)
"Hainan form/Hainan-Form"
15–18 cm
Juvenile/Jungtier
photo: P.P. VAN DIJK

RT04921-4 *Sacalia quadriocellata* (SIEBENROCK, 1903)
"Mainland form/Festland-Form"
12–15 cm
♂
photo: J.B. IVERSON

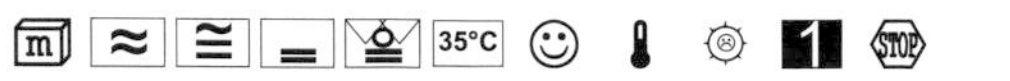

RT04922-4 *Sacalia quadriocellata* (SIEBENROCK, 1903)
"Mainland form/Festland-Form"
12–15 cm
♂ + ♀
photo: J. MARAN

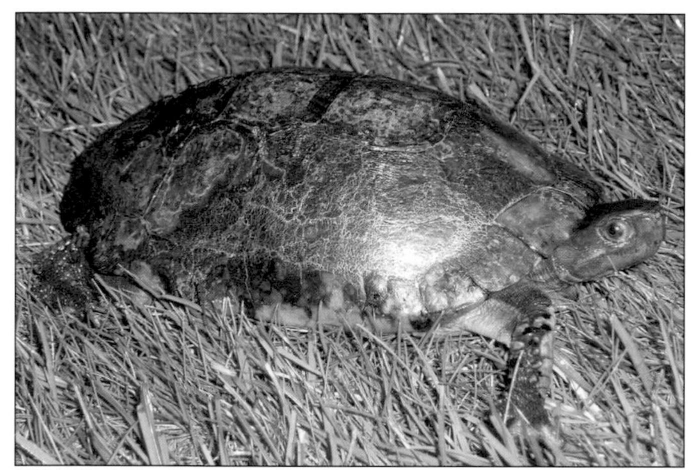

RT04923-4 *Sacalia quadriocellata* (SIEBENROCK, 1903)
"Mainland form/Festland–Form"
12–15 cm
♀
photo: T. BLANCK

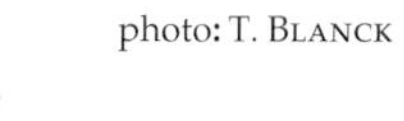

RT04924-4 *Sacalia quadriocellata* (SIEBENROCK, 1903)
"Mainland form/Festland–Form"
12–15 cm
♂
photo: T. BLANCK

RT04925-4 *Sacalia quadriocellata* (SIEBENROCK, 1903)
"Mainland form/Festland–Form"
12–15 cm
♂
photo: T. BLANCK

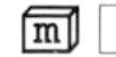

RT04931-4 *Siebenrockiella crassicollis* (Gray, 1831)
Central Thailand / Zentralthailand
18–20 cm

photo: P.P. van Dijk

RT04932-4 *Siebenrockiella crassicollis* (Gray, 1831)

18–20 cm
♂ + ♀

photo: J. Maran

RT04933-4 *Siebenrockiella crassicollis* (Gray, 1831)
18–20 cm

photo: P. Petras

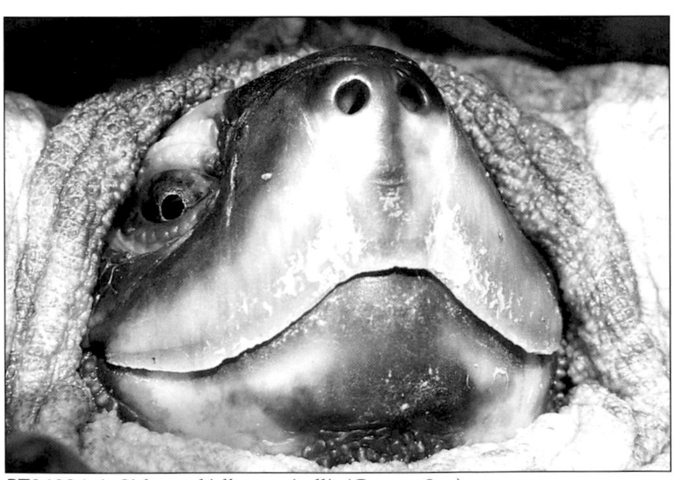

RT04934-4 *Siebenrockiella crassicollis* (Gray, 1831)

18–20 cm

photo: T. Berndt / A. Mende

Siebenrockiella crassicollis (red / rot)

RT04935-4 *Siebenrockiella crassicollis* (Gray, 1831)

18–20 cm

photo: J. Vogeltanz

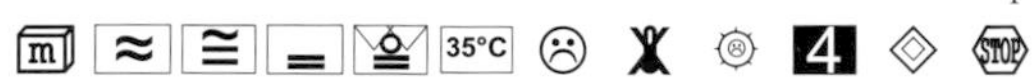

RT04936-3 *Siebenrockiella crassicollis* (Gray, 1831)

18–20 cm
Subadult

photo: J. Maran

RT04937 *Siebenrockiella crassicollis* (Gray, 1831)
Habitat, Lake Cat Tien, Vietnam
18–20 cm

photo: P.P. van Dijk

RT04941-4 *Vijayachelys silvatica* (Henderson, 1912)
Chalakudy, Kerala, India / Indien
12–14 cm
photo: S. Dattatri

RT04942-4 *Vijayachelys silvatica* (Henderson, 1912)
Anamalai, Kerala, India / Indien
12–14 cm
♂ + ♀
photo: P. Praschag

RT04943-4 *Vijayachelys silvatica* (Henderson, 1912)
Anamalai, Kerala, India / Indien
12–14 cm
photo: P. Praschag

RT04944-4 *Vijayachelys silvatica* (Henderson, 1912)
Kerala, India / Indien
12–14 cm
♂
photo: I. Das

RT04945-4 *Vijayachelys silvatica* (Henderson, 1912)
Anamalai, Kerala, India / Indien
12–14 cm
photo: P. Praschag

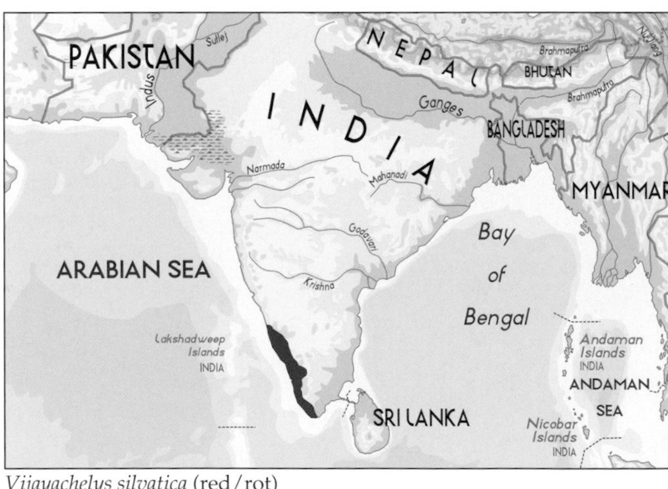

Vijayachelys silvatica (red / rot)

RT04951-4 *Platysternon megacephalum megacephalum* GRAY, 1831

18–21 cm

photo: T. BERNDT/A. MENDE

RT04952-2 *Platysternon megacephalum megacephalum* GRAY, 1831

18–21 cm
Juveniles/Jungtiere

photo: G. SCHAFFER

RT04953-4 *Platysternon megacephalum megacephalum* GRAY, 1831

18–21 cm

photo: O. BORN

RT04954-4 *Platysternon megacephalum megacephalum* GRAY, 1831
China
18–21 cm

photo: I. DAS

RT04955-4 *Platysternon megacephalum megacephalum* GRAY, 1831
China
18–21 cm

photo: I. DAS

RT04956-2 *Platysternon megacephalum megacephalum* GRAY, 1831

18–21 cm
Juvenile/Jungtier

photo: N. KAWAZOE/CREEPER

RT04961-4 *Platysternon megacephalum peguense* Gray, 1870
Thailand
18–21 cm
♂
photo: A. Nöllert

RT04962-4 *Platysternon megacephalum peguense* Gray, 1870
Thailand
18–21 cm
♂
photo: A. Nöllert

RT04963-4 *Platysternon megacephalum peguense* Gray, 1870
Phu Luang W.S. Loei, Thailand
18–21 cm
photo: P.P. van Dijk

RT04964-4 *Platysternon megacephalum peguense* Gray, 1870
Holotype „*tristernalis*" ZSM 317/1980
18–21 cm
photo: M. Franzen

RT04965-1 *Platysternon megacephalum peguense* Gray, 1870
18–21 cm
Hatchlings/Schlüpflinge
photo: N. Kawazoe/CREEPER

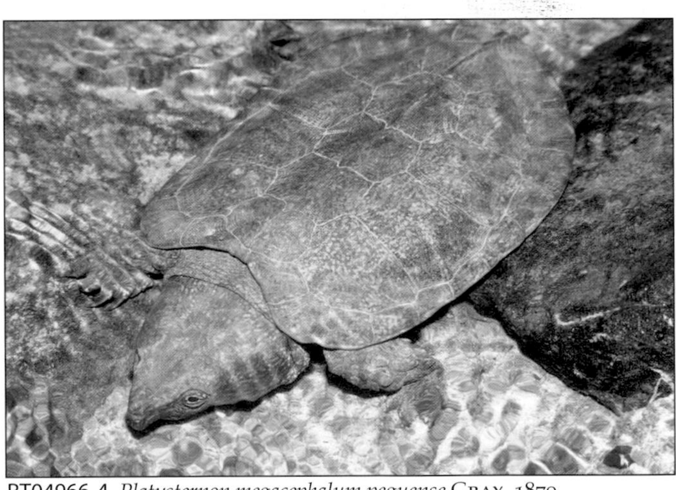

RT04966-4 *Platysternon megacephalum peguense* Gray, 1870
Phu Luang W.S. Loei, Thailand
18–21 cm
photo: P.P. van Dijk

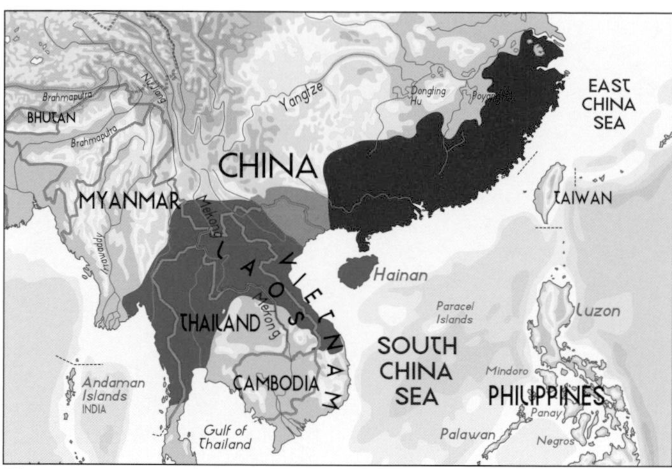

Platysternon megacephalum megacephalum (red / rot)
Platysternon megacephalum peguense (blue / blau)
Platysternon megacephalum shiui (orange)

RT04971-4 *Platysternon megacephalum shiui* Ernst & McCord, 1987
N Vietnam
18–21 cm

photo: J. Maran

RT04972 *Platysternon megacephalum shiui* Ernst & McCord, 1987
Habitat, N Vietnam

photo: J. Maran

RT04973-4 *Platysternon megacephalum shiui* Ernst & McCord, 1987

18–21 cm

photo: J. Maran

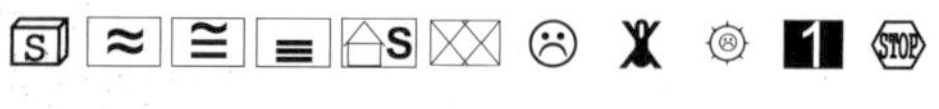

RT04974-4 *Platysternon megacephalum shiui* Ernst & McCord, 1987

18–21 cm

photo: J. Maran

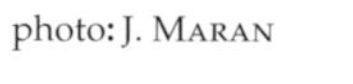

RT04981-4 *Geochelone elegans* (SCHOEPFF, 1794)
"South Indian form/Südindische Form"
20–25 cm
photo: T. BLANCK

RT04982-4 *Geochelone elegans* (SCHOEPFF, 1794)
"South Indian form/Südindische Form"
20–25 cm
photo: T. BLANCK

RT04983-4 *Geochelone elegans* (SCHOEPFF, 1794)
"South Indian form/Südindische Form"
Vadanemmeli, Tamil Nadu, India/Indien
20–25 cm
photo: I. DAS

RT04984 *Geochelone elegans* (SCHOEPFF, 1794)
"South Indian form/Südindische Form"
Vadanemmeli, Tamil Nadu, India/Indien
photo: P.P. VAN DIJK

RT04985-2 *Geochelone elegans* (SCHOEPFF, 1794)
"South Indian form/Südindische Form"
30–38 cm
Juvenile/Jungtier
photo: P.P. VAN DIJK

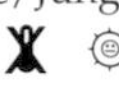

RT04986-2 *Geochelone elegans* (SCHOEPFF, 1794)
"South Indian form/Südindische Form"
30–38 cm
Juvenile/Jungtier
photo: F. HUMMEL

RT04991-4 *Geochelone elegans* (SCHOEPFF, 1794)
"Sri Lanka form/Sri–Lanka–Form"
30–38 cm

photo: A. NÖLLERT

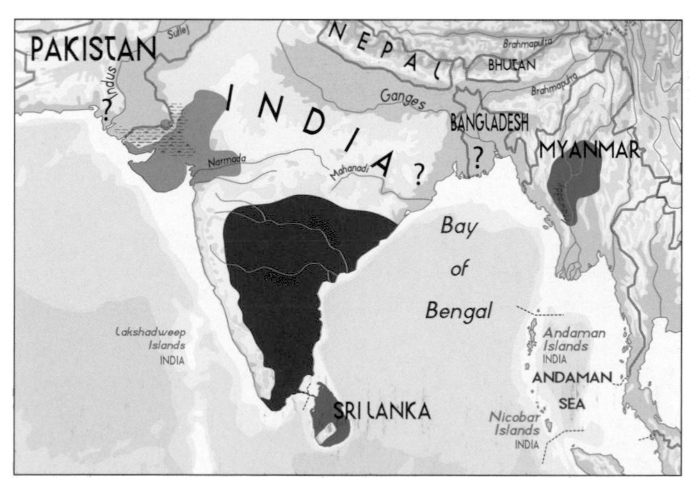

Geochelone elegans "South Indian form/Südindische Form" (red/rot)
Geochelone elegans "Sri Lanka form/Sri-Lanka-Form" (blue/blau)
Geochelone elegans "West Indian form/Westindische Form" (orange)
Geochelone platynota (green/grün)
?: questionable occurrence/Vorkommen fraglich

RT04992-4 *Geochelone elegans* (SCHOEPFF, 1794)
"Sri Lanka form/Sri–Lanka–Form"
30–38 cm

photo: A. NÖLLERT

RT04993-4 *Geochelone elegans* (SCHOEPFF, 1794)
"Sri Lanka form / Sri-Lanka-Form"
30–38 cm
photo: P. SCHÖNECKER

RT04994-4 *Geochelone elegans* (SCHOEPFF, 1794)
"Sri Lanka form / Sri-Lanka-Form"
30–38 cm
photo: B. WOLFF

RT05001-4 *Geochelone elegans* (SCHOEPFF, 1794)
"West Indian form / Westindische Form"
Gujarat, India / Indien
30–35 cm
photo: P. PRASCHAG

RT05002-4 *Geochelone elegans* (SCHOEPFF, 1794)
"West Indian form / Westindische Form"
Gujarat, India / Indien
30–35 cm
photo: P. PRASCHAG

RT05011-4 *Geochelone platynota* (BLYTH, 1863)

24–26 cm
photo: T. BLANCK

RT05012-4 *Geochelone platynota* (BLYTH, 1863)

24–26 cm
photo: B. WOLFF

RT05013-4 *Geochelone platynota* (Blyth, 1863)

24–26 cm
♂ + ♀
photo: J. Maran

RT05014-4 *Geochelone platynota* (Blyth, 1863)

24–26 cm
Mating/Paarung
photo: C. Schneiter

RT05015-1 *Geochelone platynota* (Blyth, 1863)

24–26 cm
Hatching/Schlupf
photo: C. Schneiter

RT05016-1 *Geochelone platynota* (Blyth, 1863)

24–26 cm
Hatchling/Schlüpfling
photo: C. Schneiter

RT05017-1 *Geochelone platynota* (Blyth, 1863)

24–26 cm
Hatchling/Schlüpfling
photo: C. Schneiter

RT05018-2 *Geochelone platynota* (Blyth, 1863)

24–26 cm
photo: T. Blanck

RT05021-4 *Indotestudo elongata* (Blyth, 1853)
Vietnam
28–36 cm
♀
photo: J. Maran

RT05022-4 *Indotestudo elongata* (Blyth, 1853)
Vietnam
28–36 cm
♂ + ♀
photo: J. Maran

RT05023-4 *Indotestudo elongata* (Blyth, 1853)

28–36 cm
♂
photo: J. Maran

RT05024-4 *Indotestudo elongata* (Blyth, 1853)
Huai Kha Khaeng W.S., Uthai Thani,Thailand
28–36 cm
♂
photo: P.P. van Dijk

RT05025-4 *Indotestudo elongata* (Blyth, 1853)
Huai Kha Khaeng W.S., Uthai Thani,Thailand
28–36 cm
♂
photo: P.P van Dijk

RT05026-4 *Indotestudo elongata* (Blyth, 1853)
Thailand
28–36 cm
photo: M. Mähn

RT05027-4 *Indotestudo elongata* (BLYTH, 1853)
Chitwan NP, Nepal
28–36 cm

photo: O. BORN

RT05028-4 *Indotestudo elongata* (BLYTH, 1853)
Mandalay, Myanmar
28–36 cm

photo: I. DAS

RT05029-2 *Indotestudo elongata* (BLYTH, 1853)
Thailand
28–36 cm
Juvenile/Jungtier

photo: M. MÄHN

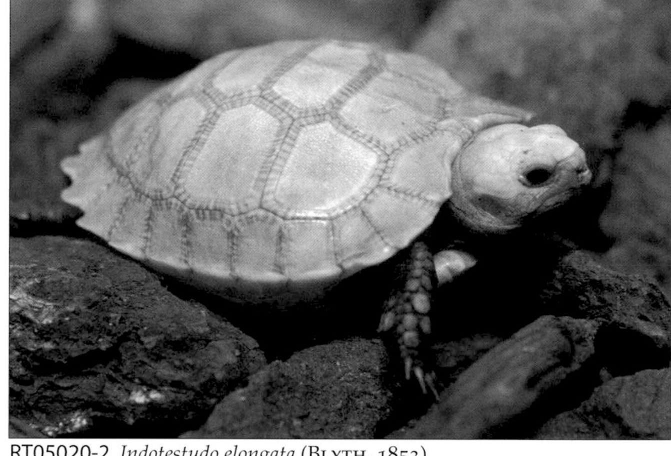

RT05020-2 *Indotestudo elongata* (BLYTH, 1853)

28–36 cm
Juvenile/Jungtier

photo: J. MARAN

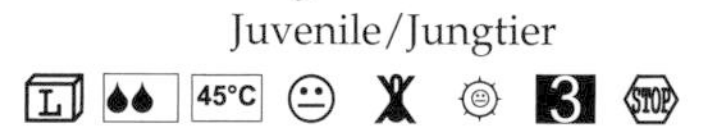

RT0502X *Indotestudo elongata* (BLYTH, 1853)
Habitat, Huai Kha Khaeng W.S., Uthai Thani,Thailand

photo: P.P VAN DIJK

Indotestudo elongata (red/rot)
Indotestudo forstenii (orange)
Indotestudo travancorica (blue/blau)
?: questionable occurrence/Vorkommen fraglich

RT05031-4 *Indotestudo forstenii* (SCHLEGEL & MÜLLER, 1845)

28–31 cm
♀
photo: J. MARAN

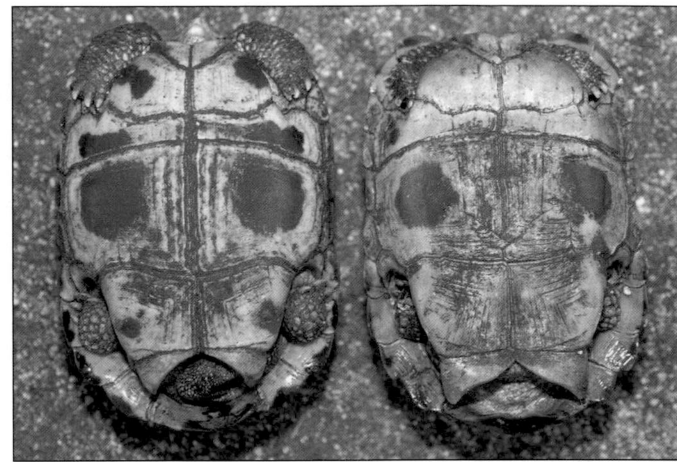

RT05032-4 *Indotestudo forstenii* (SCHLEGEL & MÜLLER, 1845)

28–31 cm
♂ + ♀
photo: J. MARAN

RT05033-4 *Indotestudo forstenii* (SCHLEGEL & MÜLLER, 1845)

28–31 cm
photo: M. ROGNER

RT05034-4 *Indotestudo forstenii* (SCHLEGEL & MÜLLER, 1845)

28–31 cm
♂
photo: J. MARAN

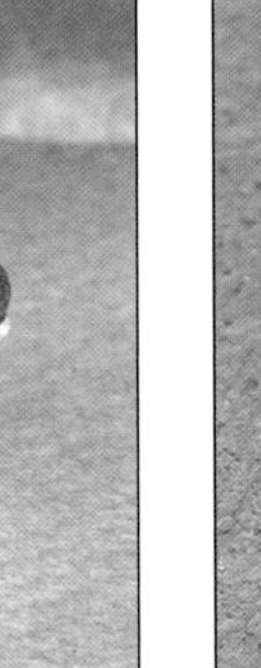

RT05035-1 *Indotestudo forstenii* (SCHLEGEL & MÜLLER, 1845)

28–31 cm
Hatchling/Schlüpfling
photo: J.H. HARDING

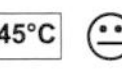

RT05036-2 *Indotestudo forstenii* (SCHLEGEL & MÜLLER, 1845)

28–31 cm
Juvenile/Jungtier
photo: P.P. VAN DIJK

RT05041-4 *Indotestudo travancorica* (BOULENGER, 1907)

30–34 cm

photo: M. MÄHN

RT05042-4 *Indotestudo travancorica* (BOULENGER, 1907)

30–34 cm
♀

photo: P. PRASCHAG

RT05043-4 *Indotestudo travancorica* (BOULENGER, 1907)
Western Ghats, India / Indien
30–34 cm

photo: I. DAS

RT05044-4 *Indotestudo travancorica* (BOULENGER, 1907)
Western Ghats, India / Indien
30–34 cm

photo: I. DAS

RT05045-2 *Indotestudo travancorica* (BOULENGER, 1907)
Anamalai, Kerala, India / Anamalai, Kerala,Indien
30–34 cm
Juvenile / Jungtier

photo: P. PRASCHAG

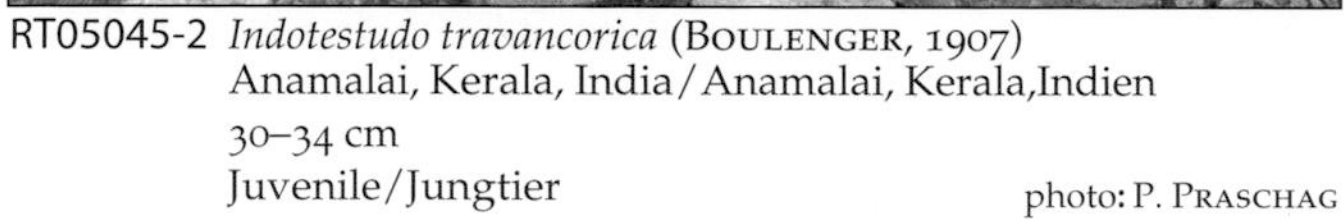

RT05046-4 *Indotestudo travancorica* (BOULENGER, 1907)
Anamalai, Kerala, India / Anamalai, Kerala,Indien
30–34 cm

photo: P. PRASCHAG

RT05051-4 *Manouria emys emys* (Schlegel & Müller, 1840)
Sarawak, Malaysia
40–50 cm
photo: I. Das

RT05052-4 *Manouria emys emys* (Schlegel & Müller, 1840)
Sumatra, Indonesia/Indonesien
40–50 cm
photo: M. Mähn

RT05053-4 *Manouria emys emys* (Schlegel & Müller, 1840)
Bhetong Bird Park, Yala, Thailand
40–50 cm
photo: P.P. van Dijk

RT05054-4 *Manouria emys emys* (Schlegel & Müller, 1840)
40–50 cm
Mating/Paarung
photo: F. Hummel

RT05055-1 *Manouria emys emys* (Schlegel & Müller, 1840)
Sumatra, Indonesia/Indonesien
40–50 cm
Hatchling/Schlüpfling
photo: M. Mähn

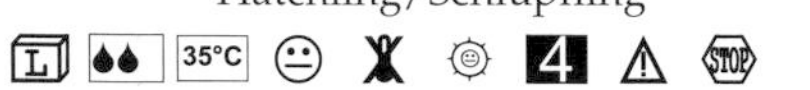

RT05056-2 *Manouria emys emys* (Schlegel & Müller, 1840)
Sumatra, Indonesia/Indonesien
40–50 cm
Juvenile/Jungtier
photo: M. Mähn

RT05061-4 *Manouria emys phayrei* (Blyth, 1853)

50–60 cm

photo: M. Mähn

RT05062-4 *Manouria emys phayrei* (Blyth, 1853)
Thailand
50–60 cm

photo: I. Das

Manouria emys emys (red/rot)
Manouria emys phayrei (blue/blau)
areas of intergradation/Intergradationszonen (pink)
?: questionable occurrence/Vorkommen fraglich

RT05063-4 *Manouria emys phayrei* (Blyth, 1853)
Thailand
50–60 cm

photo: S. Szymanski

RT05071-4 *Manouria impressa* (GÜNTHER, 1882)
Vietnam
25–31 cm
photo: J. MARAN

RT05072-4 *Manouria impressa* (GÜNTHER, 1882)
Vietnam
25–31 cm
♂ + ♀
photo: J. MARAN

RT05073-4 *Manouria impressa* (GÜNTHER, 1882)
Vietnam
25–31 cm
♂
photo: T. BLANCK

RT05074-4 *Manouria impressa* (GÜNTHER, 1882)
Vietnam
25–31 cm
♂
photo: J. MARAN

RT05075-2 *Manouria impressa* (GÜNTHER, 1882)
Vietnam
25–31 cm
Juvenile/Jungtier
photo: J.H. HARDING

RT05076-2 *Manouria impressa* (GÜNTHER, 1882)
Vietnam
25–31 cm
Juvenile/Jungtier
photo: J. MARAN

RT05077-4 *Manouria impressa* (GÜNTHER, 1882)

25–31 cm

photo: M. MÄHN

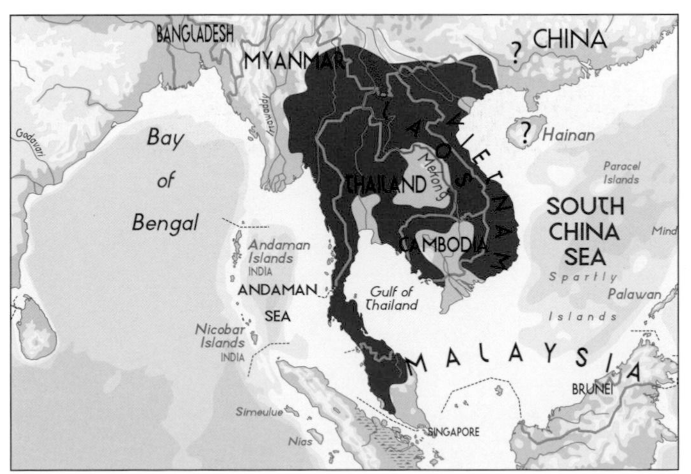

Manouria impressa (red/rot;
?: questionable occurrence/Vorkommen fraglich)

RT05078 *Manouria impressa* (GÜNTHER, 1882)
Habitat, Phu Luang, W.S., Loei, Thailand

photo: P.P. VAN DIJK

RT05081-4 *Amyda cartilaginea* (BODDAERT, 1770)
"Borneo–Sumatra form / Borneo–Sumatra–Form"
West Kalimantan, Borneo, Indonesia / Indonesien
70–83 cm
photo: M. AULIYA

RT05082-4 *Amyda cartilaginea* (BODDAERT, 1770)
"Borneo–Sumatra form / Borneo–Sumatra–Form"
West Kalimantan, Borneo, Indonesia / Indonesien
70–83 cm
photo: M. AULIYA

RT05083-4 *Amyda cartilaginea* (BODDAERT, 1770)
"Borneo–Sumatra form / Borneo–Sumatra–Form"
Balai Ringin, Sarawak, Malaysia
70–83 cm
photo: I. DAS

RT05091-4 *Amyda cartilaginea* (BODDAERT, 1770)
"Mainland form / Festland–Form"
Myanmar
70–83 cm
photo: G. KUCHLING

RT05092-4 *Amyda cartilaginea* (BODDAERT, 1770)
"Mainland form / Festland–Form" – Vietnam
70–83 cm
♀
photo: J. MARAN

RT05093-4 *Amyda cartilaginea* (BODDAERT, 1770)
"Mainland form / Festland–Form" – Vietnam
70–83 cm
♀
photo: J. MARAN

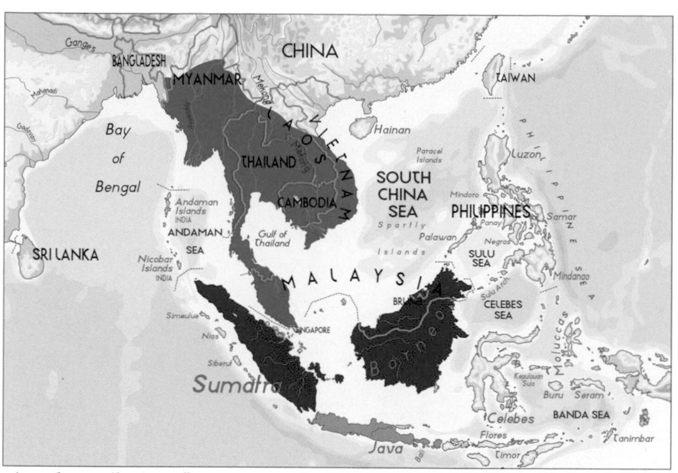

Amyda cartilaginea "Borneo-Sumatra form/Borneo-Sumatra-Form" (red/rot)
Amyda cartilaginea "Java form/Java-Form" (orange)
Amyda cartilaginea "Mainland form/Festland-Form" (blue/blau)
?: questionable occurrence/Vorkommen fraglich

RT05094-2 *Amyda cartilaginea* (BODDAERT, 1770)
"Mainland form/Festland–Form"
Nakhon Sawan, Thailand
70–83 cm – Juvenile/Jungtier
photo: P.P. VAN DIJK

RT05095-1 *Amyda cartilaginea* (BODDAERT, 1770)
"Mainland form/Festland–Form" – Thailand
70–83 cm
Hatchling/Schlüpfling
photo: P.P. VAN DIJK

RT05096-2 *Amyda cartilaginea* (BODDAERT, 1770)
"Mainland form/Festland–Form" – Vietnam
70–83 cm
Juvenile/Jungtier
photo: J. MARAN

RT05097 *Amyda cartilaginea* (BODDAERT, 1770)
"Mainland form/Festland–Form"
Habitat, Huai Kha Khaeng W.S., Uthai Thani,Thailand
photo: P.P. VAN DIJK

RT05098 *Amyda cartilaginea* (BODDAERT, 1770)
"Mainland form/Festland–Form"
Habitat, Cat Tien River, Vietnam
photo: P.P. VAN DIJK

RT05111-4 *Aspideretes gangeticus* (Cuvier, 1825)
Assam, India/Indien
80–94 cm

photo: P. Praschag

RT05112-4 *Aspideretes gangeticus* (Cuvier, 1825)
Chambal River, Madhya Pradesh, India/Indien
80–94 cm
♂

photo: E.O. Moll

RT05113-4 *Aspideretes gangeticus* (Cuvier, 1825)
Chambal River, Madhya Pradesh, India/Indien
80–94 cm

photo: I. Das

RT05114-4 *Aspideretes gangeticus* (Cuvier, 1825)
NE India/NO-Indien
80–94 cm

photo: P. Praschag

RT05115-1 *Aspideretes gangeticus* (Cuvier, 1825)
India/Indien
80–94 cm
Hatchling/Schlüpfling

photo: I. Das

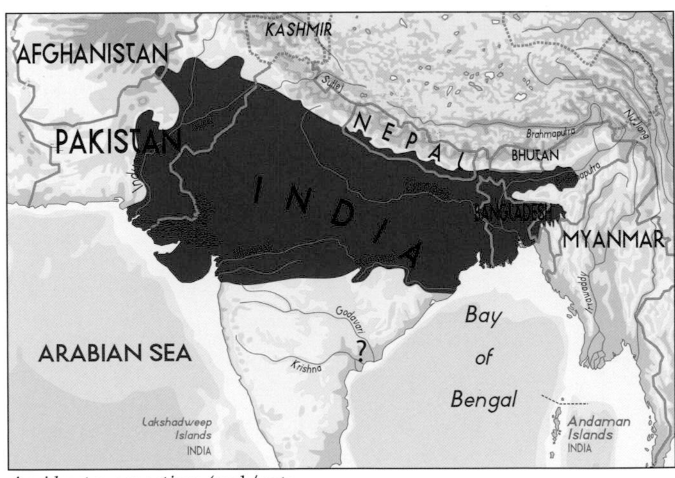

Aspideretes gangeticus (red/rot;
?: questionable occurrence/Vorkommen fraglich)

RT05121-4 *Aspideretes hurum* (GRAY, 1831)

50–60 cm

photo: I. DAS

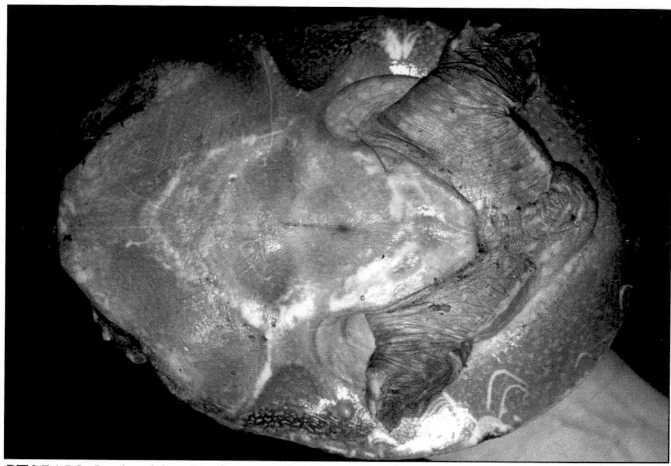

RT05122-3 *Aspideretes hurum* (GRAY, 1831)
Bangladesh/Bangladesch
50–60 cm
Subadult

photo: P. PRASCHAG

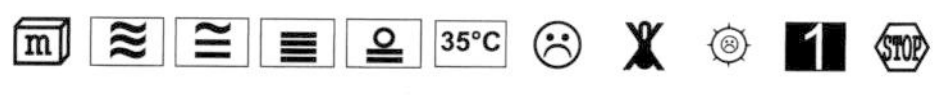

RT05123-4 *Aspideretes hurum* (GRAY, 1831)
Bangladesh/Bangladesch
50–60 cm

photo: P. PRASCHAG

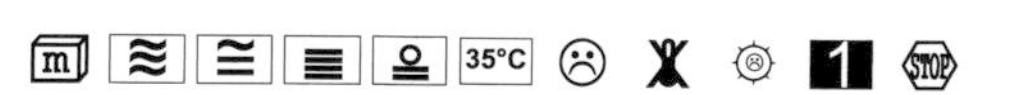

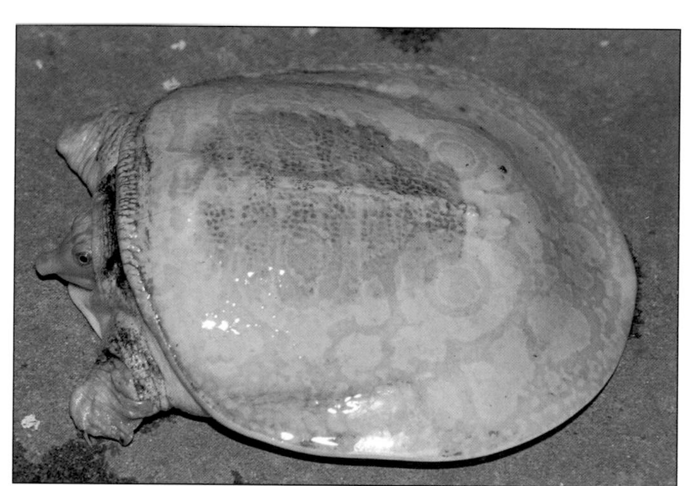

RT05124-4 *Aspideretes hurum* (GRAY, 1831)

50–60 cm

photo: S. SEKI

RT05125-2 *Aspideretes hurum* (GRAY, 1831)

50–60 cm
Juvenile/Jungtier

photo: S. SEKI

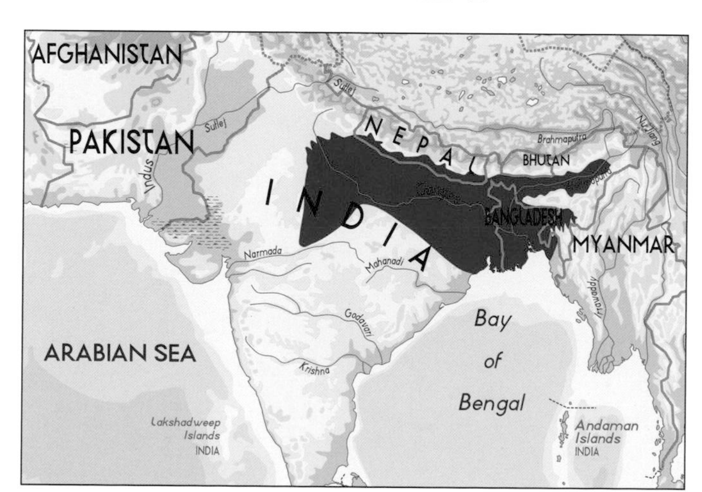

Aspideretes hurum (red/rot)

RT05131-4 *Aspideretes leithii* (GRAY, 1872)
Maharashtra, India/Indien
55–64 cm
photo: P. PRASCHAG

RT05132-4 *Aspideretes leithii* (GRAY, 1872)

55–64 cm
photo: I. DAS

RT05133-3 *Aspideretes leithii* (GRAY, 1872)

55–64 cm
Subadult
photo: P. PRASCHAG

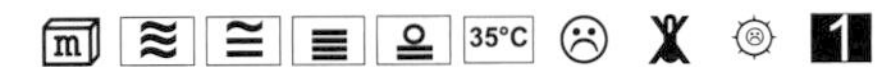

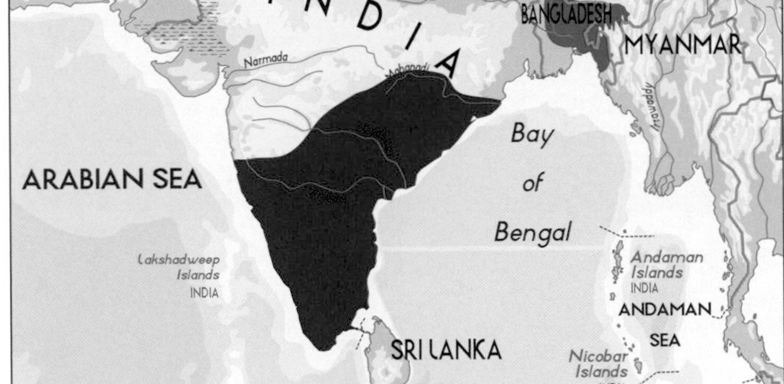

Aspideretes leithii (red/rot), *Aspideretes nigricans* (blue/blau)

RT05141-4 *Aspideretes nigricans* (ANDERSON, 1875)
Chittagong, Bangladesh/Bangladesch
80–91 cm
photo: I. DAS

RT05142-4 *Aspideretes nigricans* (ANDERSON, 1875)

80–91 cm
photo: S. SEKI

RT05143-4 *Aspideretes nigricans* (ANDERSON, 1875)
Biswanat, Assam, India/Indien
80–91 cm
♂
photo: P. PRASCHAG

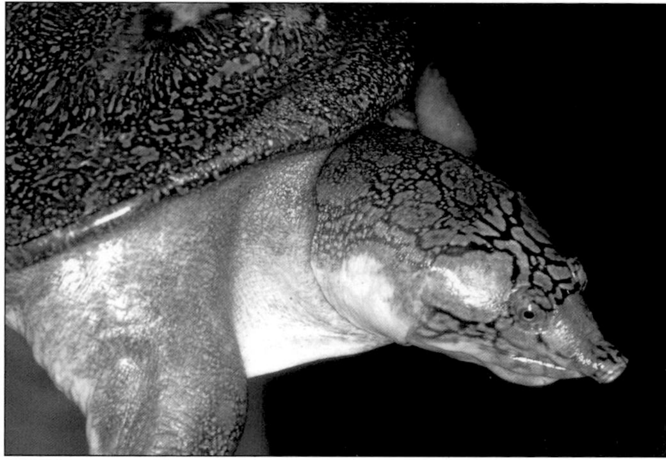

RT05144-4 *Aspideretes nigricans* (ANDERSON, 1875)

80–91 cm
photo: P. PRASCHAG

RT05145-2 *Aspideretes nigricans* (ANDERSON, 1875)

80–91 cm
Juvenile/Jungtier
photo: P. PRASCHAG

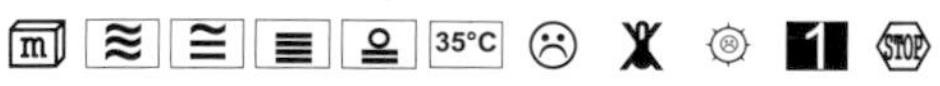

RT05146-2 *Aspideretes nigricans* (ANDERSON, 1875)
Kamakhya Temple Pond, Assam, India/Indien
Juvenile/Jungtier
photo: P. PRASCHAG

RT05147-2 *Aspideretes nigricans* (ANDERSON, 1875)

80–91 cm
Juvenile/Jungtier
photo: P. PRASCHAG

RT05148 *Aspideretes nigricans* (ANDERSON, 1875)
Kamakhya Temple Pond, Assam, India/
Kamakhya-Tempelteich, Assam, Indien
photo: P. PRASCHAG

RT05151-4 *Chitra chitra chitra* NUTAPHAND, 1986
Malaysia
120–140 cm

photo: W.P. McCORD

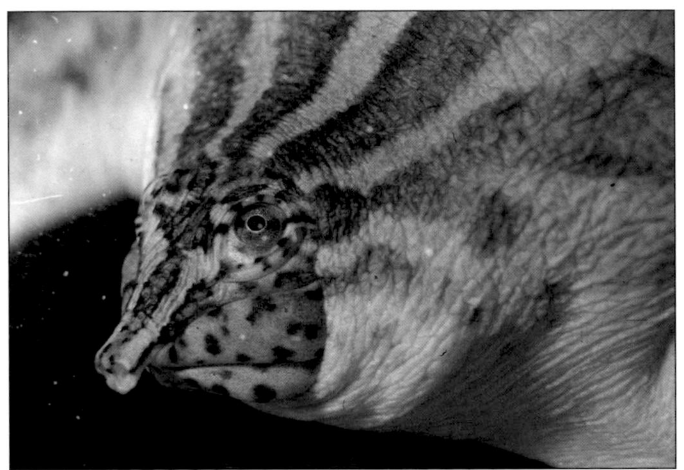

RT05152-4 *Chitra chitra chitra* NUTAPHAND, 1986
Johor, Malaysia
120–140 cm

photo: I. DAS

RT05153-4 *Chitra chitra chitra* NUTAPHAND, 1986
Mae Klong, Kanchanaburi, Thailand
120–140 cm

photo: P.P. VAN DIJK

RT05154-1 *Chitra chitra chitra* NUTAPHAND, 1986
Mae Klong, Kanchanaburi, Thailand
120–140 cm
Hatchling/Schlüpfling

photo: P.P. VAN DIJK

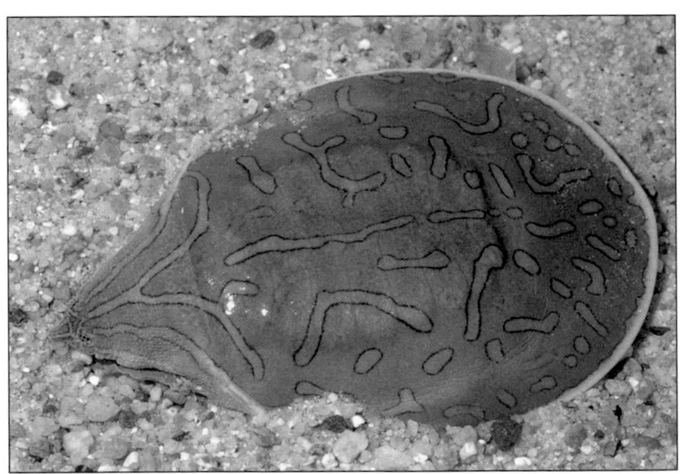

RT05155-1 *Chitra chitra chitra* NUTAPHAND, 1986
Mae Klong, Kanchanaburi, Thailand
120–140 cm
Hatchling/Schlüpfling

photo: P.P. VAN DIJK

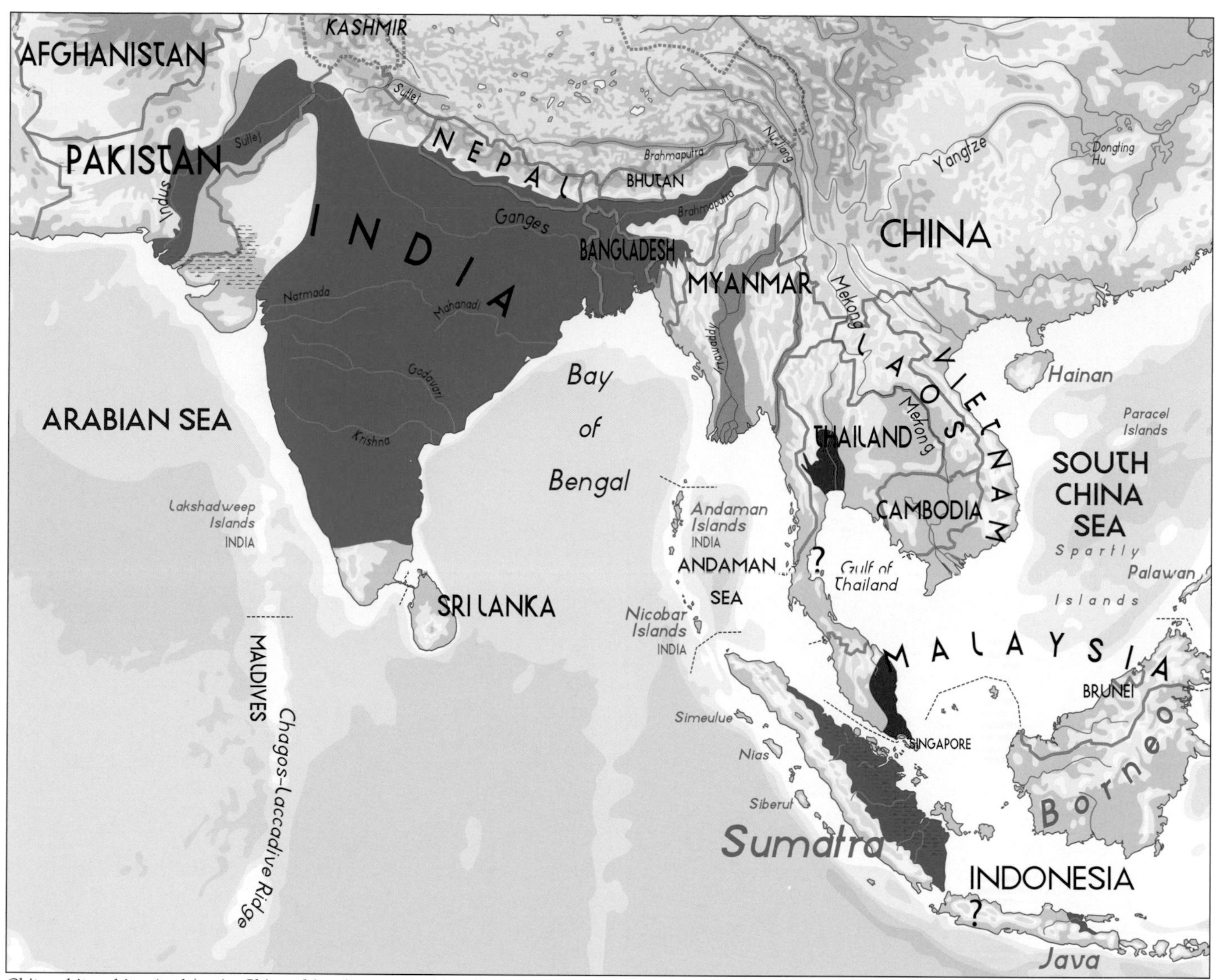

Chitra chitra chitra (red/rot); *Chitra chitra javanensis* (blue/blau); *Chitra indica* (green/grün); *Chitra vandijki* (orange);
?: questionable occurrence/Vorkommen fraglich

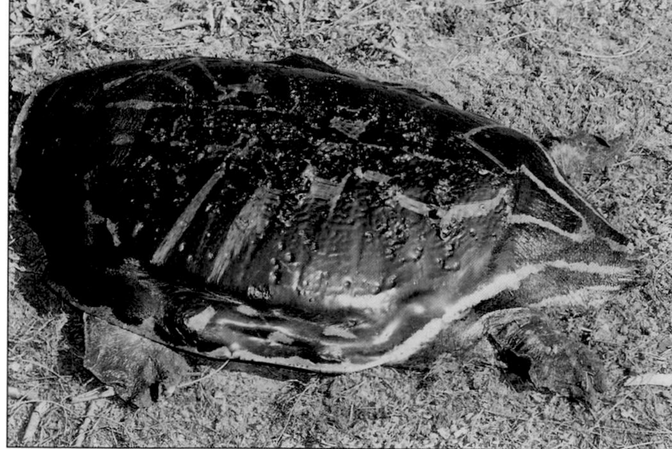

RT05161-4 *Chitra chitra javanensis* McCord & Pritchard, 2003

120–140 cm

photo: W.P. McCord

RT05162-4 *Chitra chitra javanensis* McCord & Pritchard, 2003
Java, Indonesia/Indonesien
120–140 cm

photo: I. Das

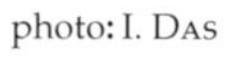

RT05171-4 *Chitra indica* (GRAY, 1831)
100–120 cm
♀
photo: J. MARAN

RT05172-4 *Chitra indica* (GRAY, 1831)
Chambal River, Madhya Pradesh, India/Indien
100–120 cm
♂
photo: E.O. MOLL

RT05173-4 *Chitra indica* (GRAY, 1831)
100–120 cm
♀
photo: J. MARAN

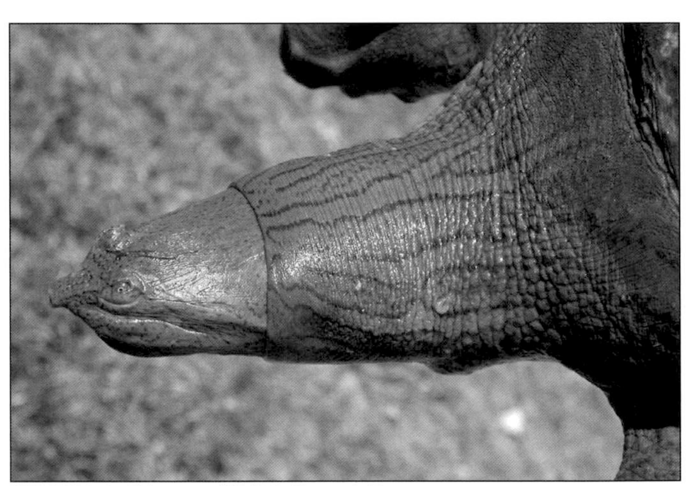

RT05181-4 *Chitra vandijki* MCCORD & PRITCHARD, 2003
Myanmar
100–120 cm
photo: G. KUCHLING

RT05182-4 *Chitra vandijki* MCCORD & PRITCHARD, 2003
Myanmar
100–120 cm
photo: G. KUCHLING

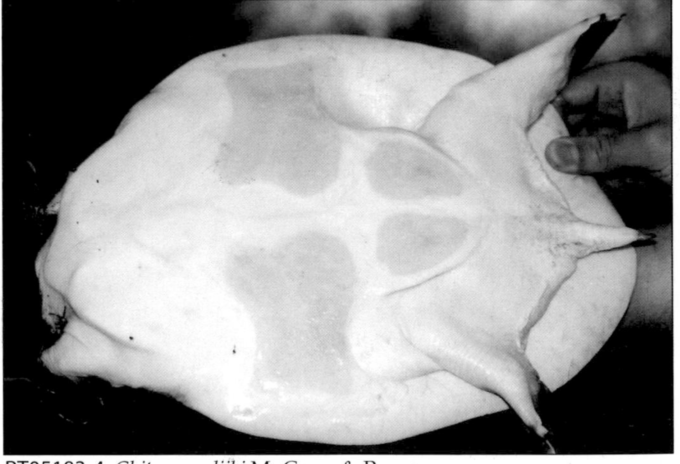

RT05183-4 *Chitra vandijki* MCCORD & PRITCHARD, 2003
Myanmar
100–120 cm
photo: W.P. MCCORD

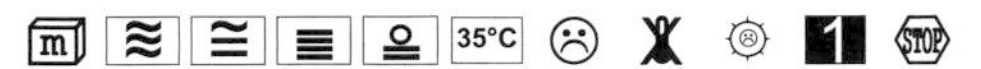

RT05191-4 *Dogania subplana* (GEOFFROY SAINT-HILAIRE, 1809)
Bau, Sarawak, Malaysia
25–31 cm

photo: I. DAS

RT05192-4 *Dogania subplana* (GEOFFROY SAINT-HILAIRE, 1809)
Thailand
25–31 cm

photo: P.P. VAN DIJK

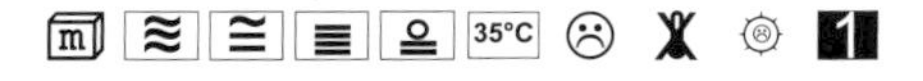

RT05193-4 *Dogania subplana* (GEOFFROY SAINT-HILAIRE, 1809)
Borneo, Indonesia/Indonesien
25–31 cm

photo: ARCHIV F.W. HENKEL

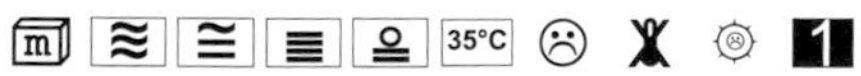

RT05194-4 *Dogania subplana* (GEOFFROY SAINT-HILAIRE, 1809)
Pulau Tioman, Pahang, Malaysia
25–31 cm

photo: I. DAS

RT05195-4 *Dogania subplana* (GEOFFROY SAINT-HILAIRE, 1809)
pigment loss syndrome/Pigment-Verlust-Syndrom
25–31 cm

photo: W. SACHSSE

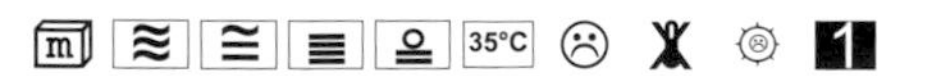

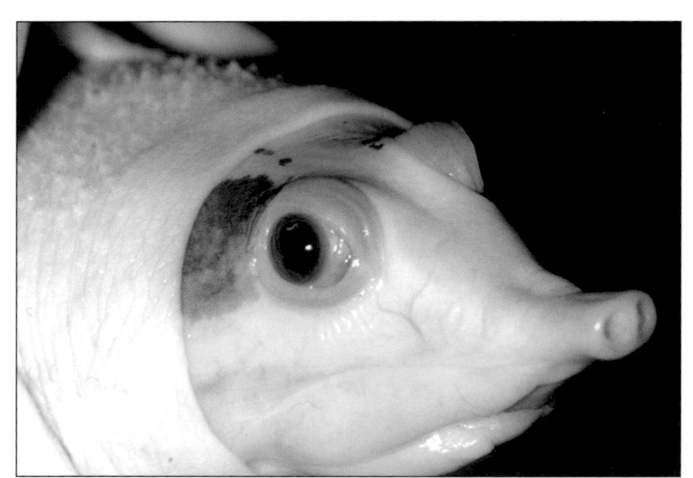

RT05196-4 *Dogania subplana* (GEOFFROY SAINT-HILAIRE, 1809)
pigment loss syndrome/Pigment-Verlust-Syndrom
25–31 cm

photo: W. SACHSSE

RT05197-4 *Dogania subplana* (GEOFFROY SAINT–HILAIRE, 1809)

25–31 cm

photo: J. MARAN

Dogania subplana (red/rot)

RT05198-2 *Dogania subplana* (GEOFFROY SAINT–HILAIRE, 1809)
Bukit Gasing, Selangor, Malaysia
25–31 cm
Juvenile/Jungtier

photo: P.P. VAN DIJK

35°C 1

RT05201-4 *Lissemys punctata punctata* (BONNATERRE, 1789)
Vadanemmeli, India/Indien
30–37 cm
photo: I. DAS

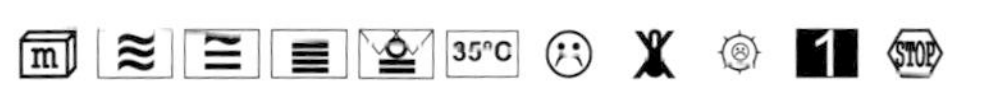

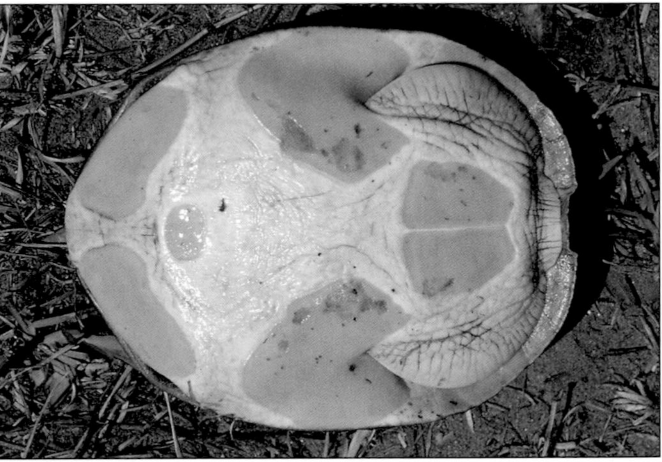

RT05202-4 *Lissemys punctata punctata* (BONNATERRE, 1789)
Vadanemmeli, Tamil Nadu, India/Indien
30–37 cm
photo: I. DAS

RT05203-4 *Lissemys punctata punctata* (BONNATERRE, 1789)
Godavari River, Andra Pradesh, India/Indien
30–37 cm
photo: P. PRASCHAG

RT05204 *Lissemys punctata punctata* (BONNATERRE, 1789)
Habitat, Vadanemmeli, Tamil Nadu, India/Indien
photo: P.P. VAN DIJK

RT05211-4 *Lissemys punctata andersoni* WEBB, 1980

30–37 cm
photo: J. MARAN

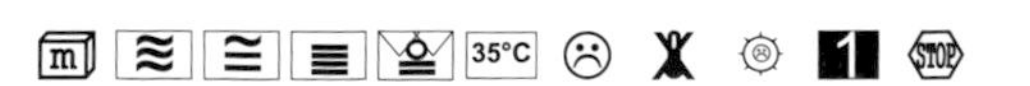

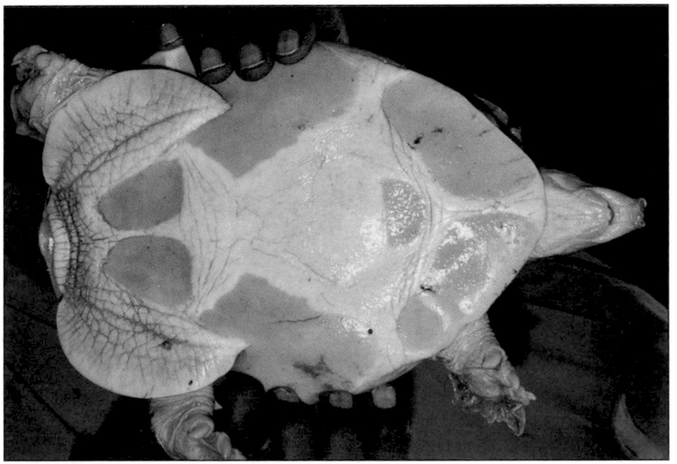

RT05212-3 *Lissemys punctata andersoni* WEBB, 1980
Kukrail, Uttar Pradesh, India/Indien
30–37 cm
Subadult
photo: P.P. VAN DIJK

RT05214-3 *Lissemys punctata andersoni* WEBB, 1980
Kukrail, Uttar Pradesh, India/Indien
30–37 cm
Subadult
photo: P.P. VAN DIJK

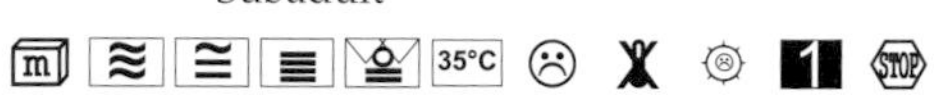

RT05215-4 *Lissemys punctata andersoni* WEBB, 1980

30–37 cm
photo: J. MARAN

RT05216-4 *Lissemys punctata andersoni* WEBB, 1980
Chitwan NP, Nepal
30–37 cm
photo: O. BORN

RT05217-2 *Lissemys punctata andersoni* WEBB, 1980
Chitwan NP, Nepal
30–37 cm
Juvenile/Jungtier
photo: N. KAWAZOE/CREEPER

RT05221-4 *Lissemys punctata* "Sri Lanka form/Sri-Lanka-Form"
Sri Lanka
30–37 cm
photo: U. THIEME

RT05222-4 *Lissemys punctata* "Sri Lanka form/Sri-Lanka-Form"
Sri Lanka
30–37 cm
photo: A. NÖLLERT

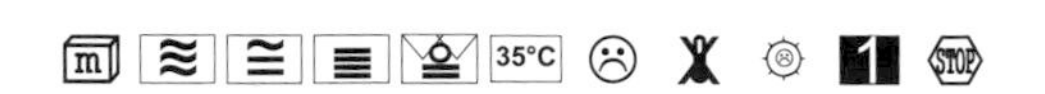

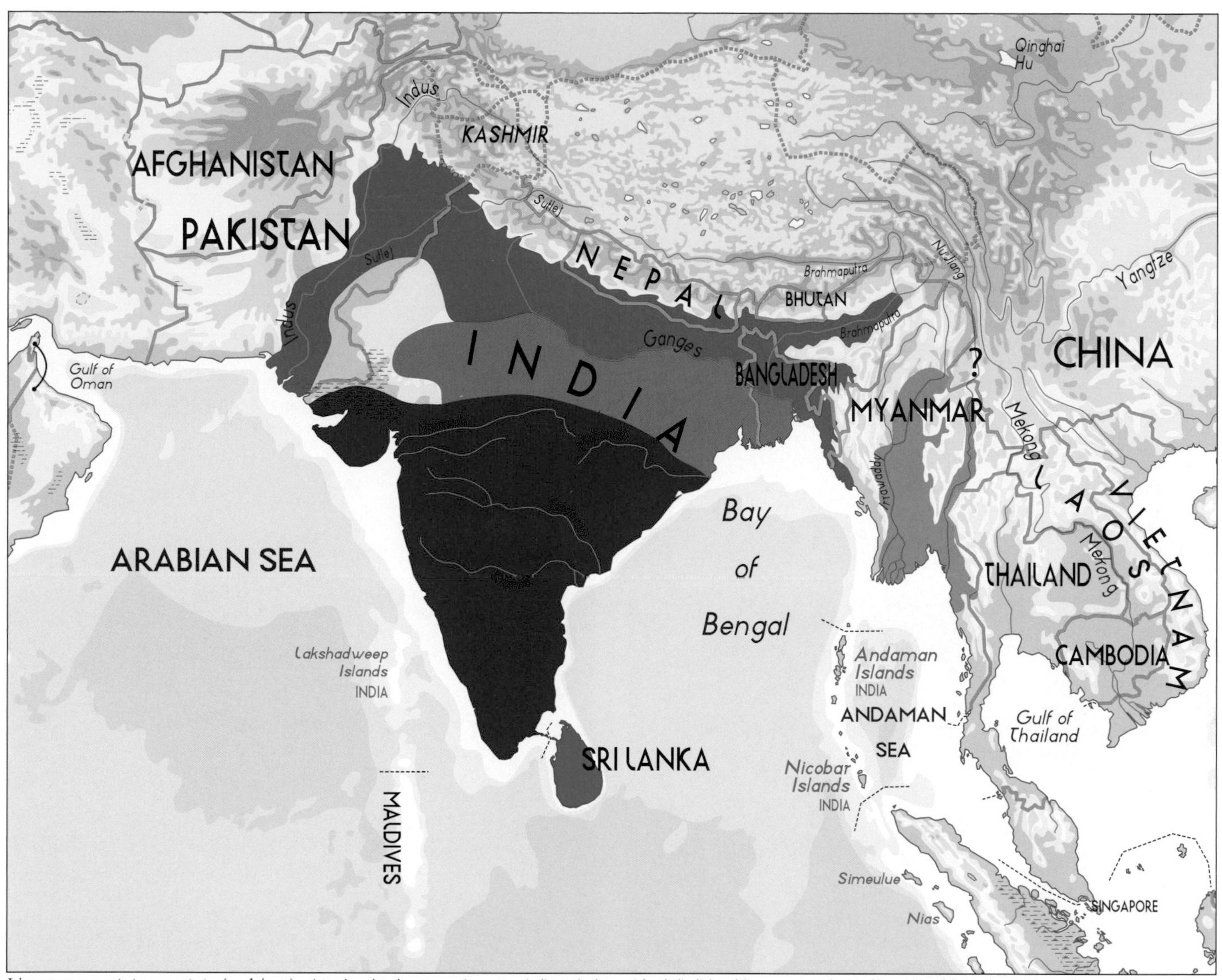

Lissemys punctata punctata (red/rot) – introduced to desert areas in western India, to Andaman Islands (India) and Singapore, not depicted here/eingeführt in den Wüstengebieten im Westen Indiens, auf den Andamanen (Indien) und in Singapur, hier nicht abgebildet
Lissemys punctata andersoni (blue/blau); *Lissemys punctata* "Sri Lankan form/Sri-Lanka-Form" (green/grün)
Lissemys scutata (orange; ?: questionable occurrence/Vorkommen fraglich)
areas of intergradation/Intergradationszonen (pink)

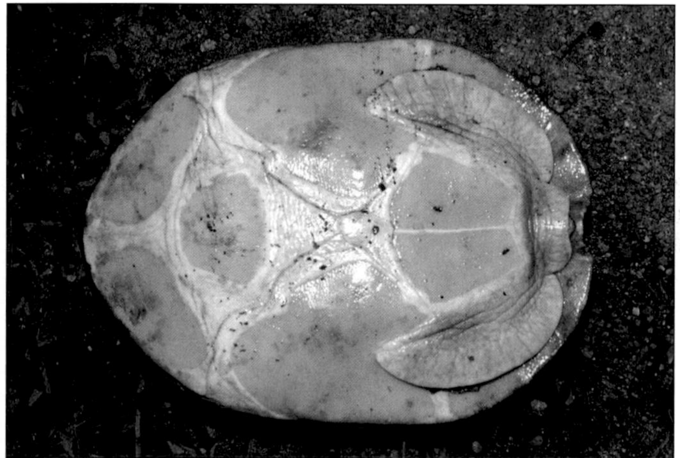

RT05223-4 *Lissemys punctata* "Sri Lanka form/Sri-Lanka-Form"
Sea Turtle Center, Bentota, Sri Lanka
30–37 cm
photo: P.P. van Dijk

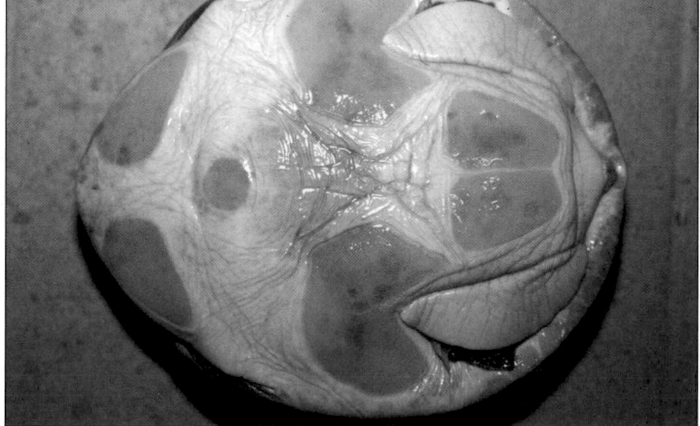

RT05231-4 *Lissemys scutata* (Peters, 1868)
20–23 cm
♀
photo: J. Maran

RT05232-4 *Lissemys scutata* (PETERS, 1868)
Myanmar
20–23 cm

photo: I. DAS

RT05233-4 *Lissemys scutata* (PETERS, 1868)
Mandalay, Myanmar
20–23 cm

photo: S. SZYMANSKI

RT05241-4 *Nilssonia formosa* (GRAY, 1869)
Myanmar
57–65 cm

photo: G. KUCHLING

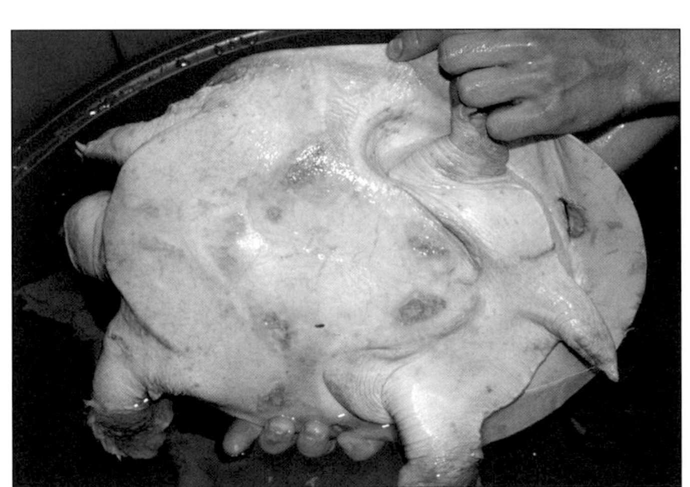

RT05242-2 *Nilssonia formosa* (GRAY, 1869)
Myanmar
57–65 cm
Juvenile/Jungtier

photo: P.P. VAN DIJK

RT05243-4 *Nilssonia formosa* (GRAY, 1869)
Myanmar
57–65 cm

photo: G. KUCHLING

RT05244-2 *Nilssonia formosa* (GRAY, 1869)
Myanmar
57–65 cm
Juvenile/Jungtier

photo: P.P. VAN DIJK

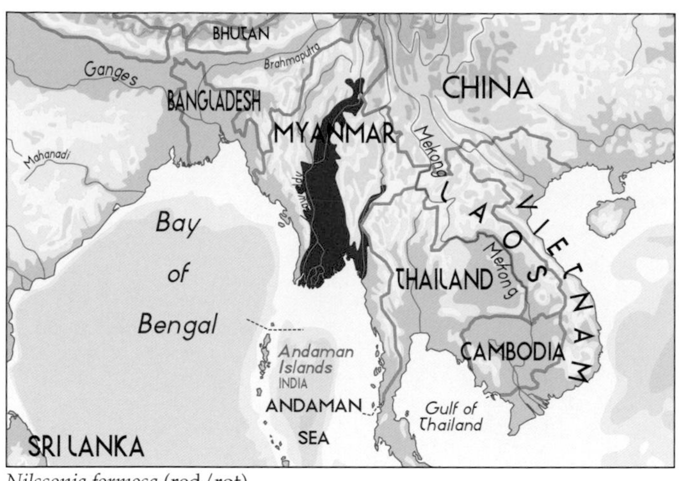

Nilssonia formosa (red / rot)

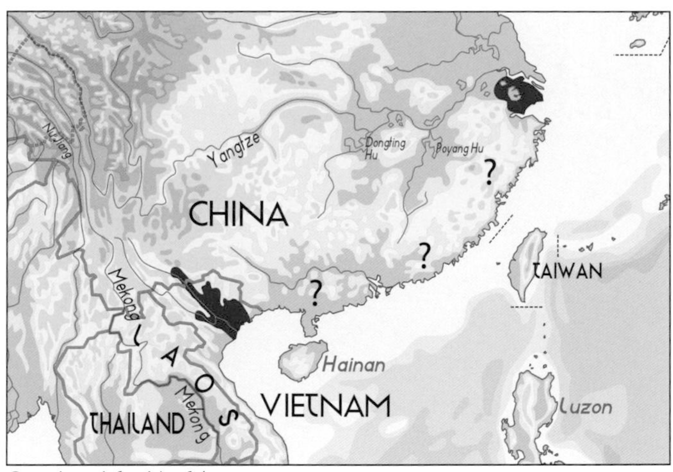

Oscaria swinhoei (red / rot;
?: questionable occurrence / Vorkommen fraglich)

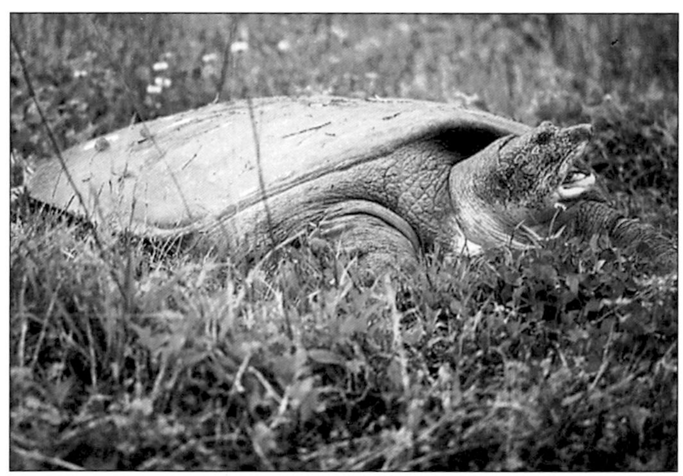

RT05251-4 *Oscaria swinhoei* GRAY, 1873

90–105 cm

photo: Z. ZHOU, courtesy of K. ADLER

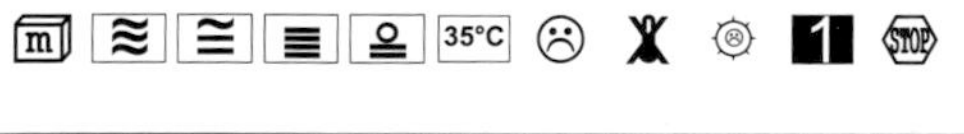

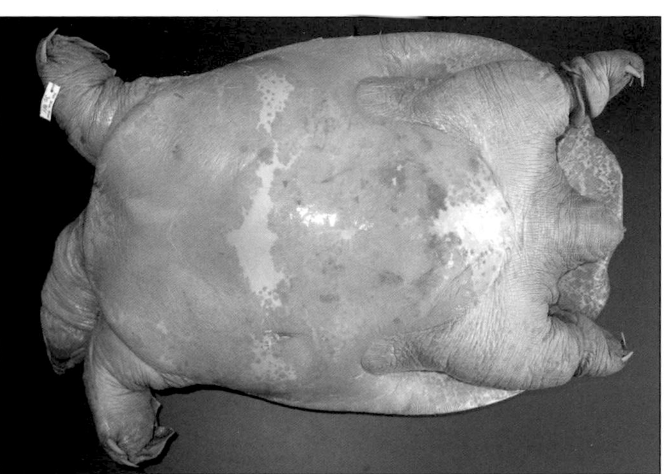

RT05252-4 *Oscaria swinhoei* GRAY, 1873
NMW 30 911
90–105 cm

photo: R. GEMEL / Naturhistorisches Museum Wien

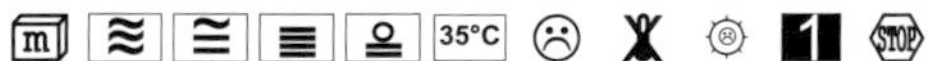

RT05253-4 *Oscaria swinhoei* GRAY, 1873
Shanghai, China
90–105 cm

photo: J. THORBJARNARSON

RT05254-4 *Oscaria swinhoei* GRAY, 1873
Hanoi, Vietnam
90–105 cm

photo: Collection D. HENDRIE

RT05261-4 *Palea steindachneri* (Siebenrock, 1906)
N Vietnam
40–50 cm
photo: T. Ziegler

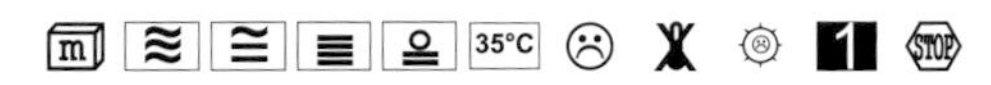

RT05262-4 *Palea steindachneri* (Siebenrock, 1906)
N Vietnam
40–50 cm
photo: T. Ziegler

RT05263-4 *Palea steindachneri* (Siebenrock, 1906)

40–50 cm
photo: B. Wolff

RT05264-4 *Palea steindachneri* (Siebenrock, 1906)
N Vietnam
40–50 cm
photo: T. Ziegler

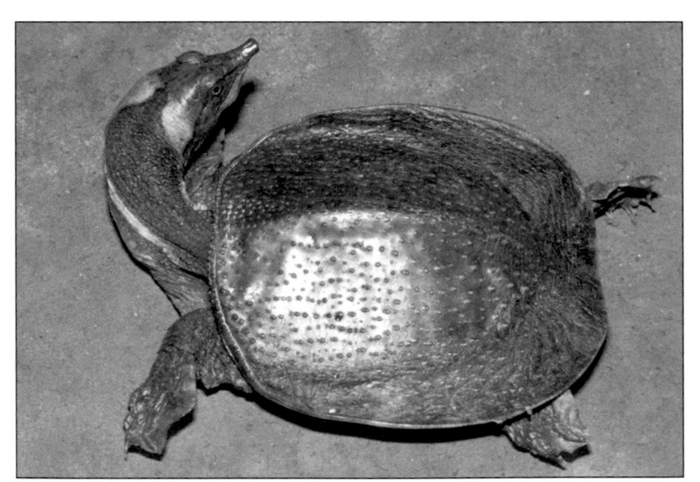

RT05265-2 *Palea steindachneri* (Siebenrock, 1906)
N Vietnam
40–50 cm
Juvenile/Jungtier
photo: T. Ziegler

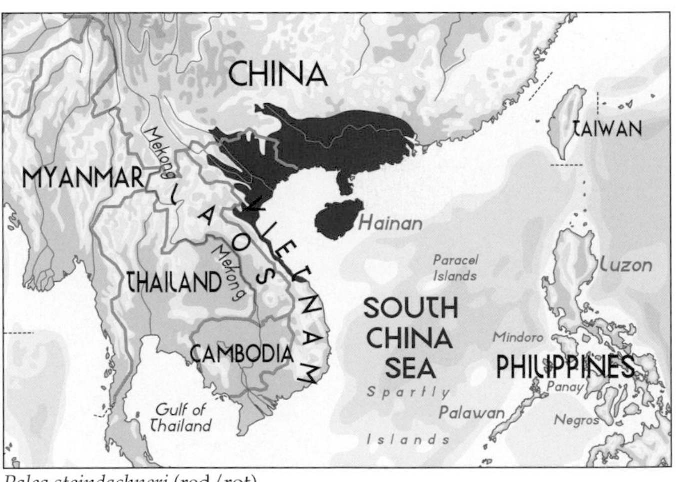

Palea steindachneri (red/rot)

RT05271-4 *Pelochelys cantorii* Gray, 1864
Terengganu River, Kg. Tabakang, Terengganu, Malaysia
190–200 cm

photo: E.O. Moll

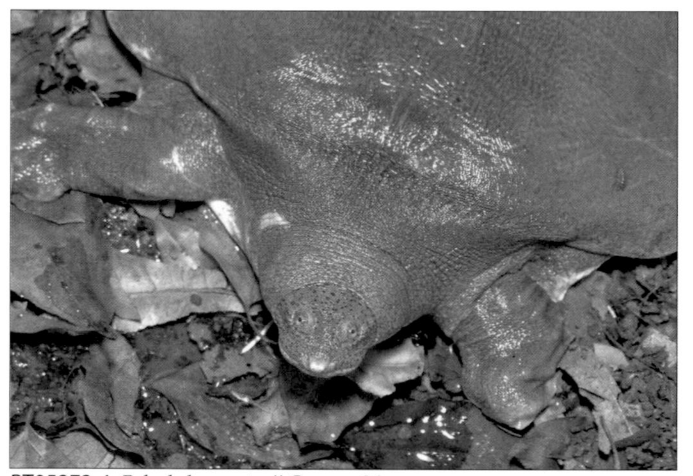

RT05273-4 *Pelochelys cantorii* Gray, 1864

190–200 cm

photo: S. Seki

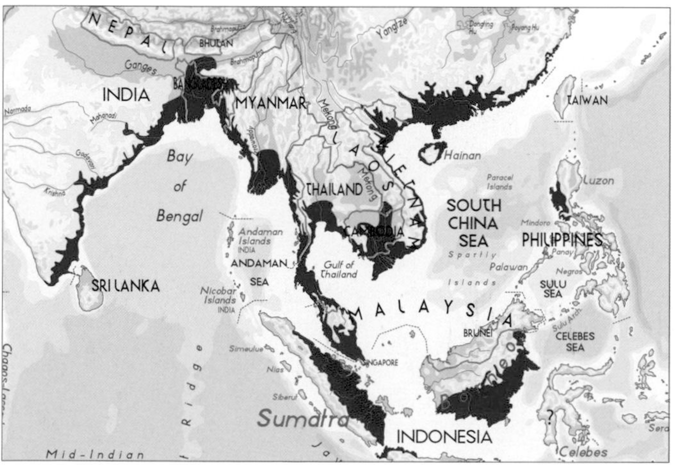

Pelochelys cantorii (red/rot;
?: questionable occurrence/Vorkommen fraglich)

RT05272-4 *Pelochelys cantorii* Gray, 1864
Penang, Malaysia
190–200 cm

photo: E.O. Moll

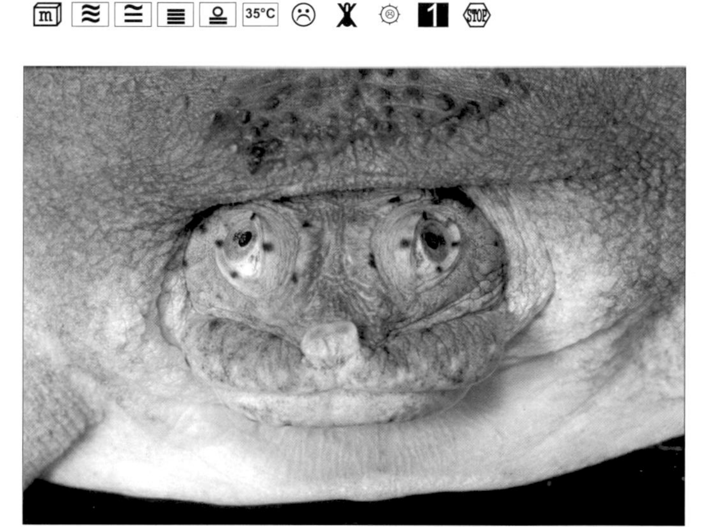

RT05274-4 *Pelochelys cantorii* Gray, 1864
Johor, Malaysia
190–200 cm

photo: I. Das

RT05275-2 *Pelochelys cantorii* Gray, 1864

190–200 cm
Juvenile/Jungtier

photo: S. Seki

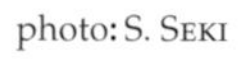

RT05281-4 *Pelodiscus maackii* (Brandt, 1858)
Bidzahn River, Russia/Russland
35–45 cm
photo: E.V. Adnagulov

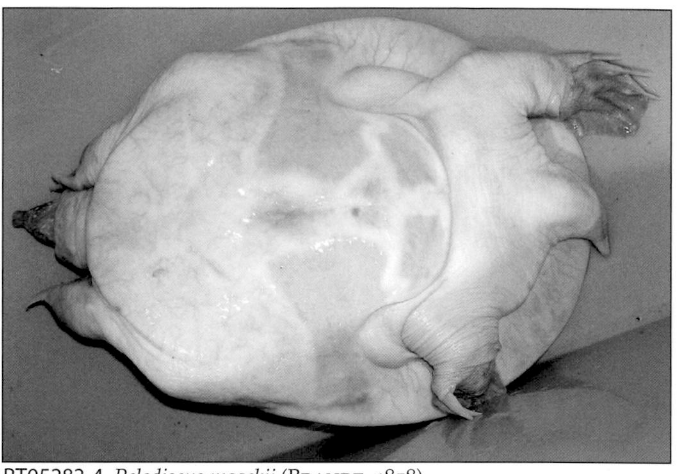

RT05282-4 *Pelodiscus maackii* (Brandt, 1858)

35–45 cm
photo: S. Seebacher

RT05283-4 *Pelodiscus maackii* (Brandt, 1858)
Primorye Region, Russia/Russland
35–45 cm
photo: Mikhailov courtesy of ABF Publishers

RT05284-4 *Pelodiscus maackii* (Brandt, 1858)

35–45 cm
photo: S. Seebacher

RT05285-4 *Pelodiscus maackii* (Brandt, 1858)
Russia/Russland
35–45 cm
photo: E.A. Dunaev

RT05283-1 *Pelodiscus maackii* (Brandt, 1858)
Bidzahn River, Russia/Russland
35–45 cm
Hatchling/Schlüpfling
photo: E.V. Adnagulov

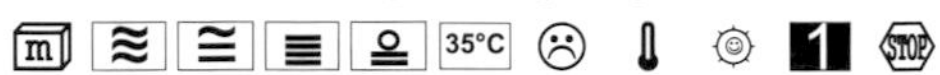

RT05291-4 *Pelodiscus sinensis* (WIEGMANN, 1835)
"Chinese form/Chinesische Form"
20–26 cm

photo: I. DAS

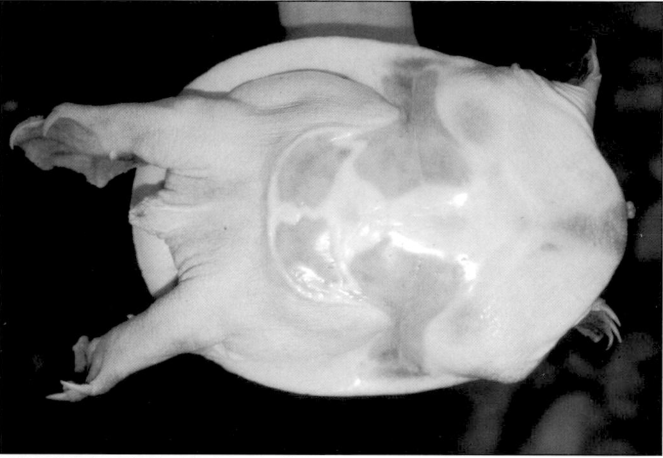

RT05292-4 *Pelodiscus sinensis* (WIEGMANN, 1835)
"Chinese form/Chinesische Form"
20–26 cm
♀

photo: J. MARAN

RT05293-4 *Pelodiscus sinensis* (WIEGMANN, 1835)
"Chinese form/Chinesische Form"
20–26 cm
♀

photo: J. MARAN

RT05294-4 *Pelodiscus sinensis* (WIEGMANN, 1835)
"Chinese form/Chinesische Form"
20–26 cm

photo: O. BORN

RT05295-1 *Pelodiscus sinensis* (WIEGMANN, 1835)
"Chinese form/Chinesische Form"
20–26 cm
Hatching/Schlupf

photo: J. MARAN

RT05296-1 *Pelodiscus sinensis* (WIEGMANN, 1835)
"Chinese form/Chinesische Form"
20–26 cm
Hatchling/Schlüpfling

photo: I. DAS

Pelodiscus maackii (red / rot; ?: questionable occurrence / Vorkommen fraglich)
Pelodiscus sinensis "Chinese form / Chinesische Form" (blue / blau) – introduced to Thailand, Indonesia, Malaysia, Singapore and several Japanese islands, not depicted here / eingeführt in Thailand, Indonesien, Malaysia und Singapur sowie auf verschiedenen japanischen Inseln, hier nicht abgebildet
Pelodiscus sinensis "Vietnamese form / Vietnamesische Form" (orange) – introduced to Cambodia, Laos and Thailand, not depicted here / eingeführt in Kambodscha, Laos und Thailand, hier nicht abgebildet

RT05301-4 *Pelodiscus sinensis* (WIEGMANN, 1835)
"Vietnamese form / Vietnamesische Form"
20–26 cm
photo: P.P. VAN DIJK

RT05302-4 *Pelodiscus sinensis* (WIEGMANN, 1835)
"Vietnamese form / Vietnamesische Form"
20–26 cm
photo: J. MARAN

RT05303-4 *Pelodiscus sinensis* (Wiegmann, 1835)
"Vietnamese form / Vietnamesische Form"
20–26 cm

photo: T. Ziegler

 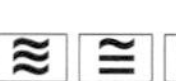    

RT05304-4 *Pelodiscus sinensis* (Wiegmann, 1835)
"Vietnamese form / Vietnamesische Form"
20–26 cm

photo: T. Ziegler

RT05305-4 *Pelodiscus sinensis* (Wiegmann, 1835)
"Vietnamese form / Vietnamesische Form"
20–26 cm

photo: T. Ziegler

 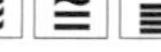    

RT05311-4 *Chelodina mccordi* RHODIN, 1994

20–22 cm

photo: O. RÖMPP

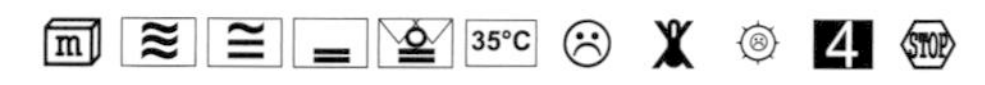

RT05312-4 *Chelodina mccordi* RHODIN, 1994
Central Roti Island, Indonesia / Zentrum der Insel Roti, Indonesien
20–22 cm

photo: C. HAGEN

RT05313-4 *Chelodina mccordi* RHODIN, 1994
Central Roti Island, Indonesia / Zentrum der Insel Roti, Indonesien
20–22 cm

photo: C. HAGEN

RT05314-4 *Chelodina mccordi* RHODIN, 1994
Eastern Roti Island, Indonesia / Osten der Insel Roti, Indonesien
20–22 cm

photo: C. HAGEN

RT05315-4 *Chelodina mccordi* RHODIN, 1994
Eastern Roti Island, Indonesia / Osten der Insel Roti, Indonesien
20–22 cm

photo: C. HAGEN

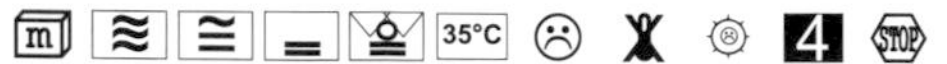

RT05316-1 *Chelodina mccordi* RHODIN, 1994

20–22 cm
Hatchling / Schlüpfling

photo: O. RÖMPP

RT05317-4 *Chelodina mccordi* RHODIN, 1994

20–22 cm

photo: O. RÖMPP

RT05318 *Chelodina mccordi* RHODIN, 1994
Habitat, Lake Temodale, Roti Island, Indonesia / Indonesien

photo: C. HAGEN

Chelodina mccordi (red / rot)

Introduction to Hybrids

The previous pages have introduced you more intimately to the incredible diversity and variation of Asian chelonians. However, on the following pages, we would like to portray an even greater diversity than that. These are the hybrids.

Hybrids are crossbreeds between different taxonomic units. Until just a few years ago it was thought that hybrid chelonians were rare incidences. This perception has now changed in a fundamental manner, and at the time this book went to print, more than one-hundred different hybrids were known from within the family Geoemydidae alone. For one, these include "artificial" hybrids, that is, crossbreeds that have been "created" by man through the deliberate pairing or joint housing of a variety of species, in particular in the large turtle breeding farms of China or the collections of amateur breeders. On the other hand, it is a rather fascinating fact that the Asian pond turtles of the family Geoemydidae also produce natural hybrids, i.e., crossbreeds that occur in the wild. Some of these hybrids are so different from their parental species that scientists were over the last two decades fooled into thinking these were new, undescribed species, which they consequently defined and named. Instances of this kind included, e.g., *Cuora serrata, Mauremys iversoni, Mauremys pritchardi, Ocadia glyphistoma,* and *Sacalia pseudocellata*. In part, these were natural hybrids, as was the case with *Cuora serrata,* which subsequently turned out to be a cross between *Pyxidea mouhotii* and *Cistoclemmys galbinifrons.* This phenomenon is referred to as "evolution in progress" and is presently explained as a process of speciation right before our eyes. But why is it happening? Probably it is a result of the enormous pressures exerted on the wild populations of most Asian chelonian species. Massive collection for the food markets of China and large-scale destruction of natural habitats appear to be the most important triggers for this development, forcing the few specimens remaining in the wild to mate with everything that remotely resembles another turtle. Other hybrid forms, such as *Mauremys iversoni,* have been created with the purpose of imitating in their color patterns *Pyxiclemmys trifasciata,* a species that demands high prices in China. Their value is much higher than that of its "mother species" *Cathaiemys mutica,* which, on the other hand, produces more eggs than genuine *Pyxiclemmys trifasciata*. As a consequence, which solution could be more obvious to shrewd Chinese businessmen than to combine the two desired traits in one "species"? Another factor has been the demand by Western scientists for new, hitherto undescribed chelonians, for which many were willing to pay large amounts of money.

Einführung zu Hybridformen

Auf den vorangegangenen Seiten haben Sie die unglaubliche Vielfalt und Variation der asiatischen Schildkröten näher kennen gelernt. Auf den nun folgenden Seiten möchten wir Ihnen noch eine deutlich größere Vielfalt präsentieren, als die, die auf diesem Kontinent ohnehin schon besteht. Die Rede ist von Hybriden. Hybriden sind Kreuzungen verschiedener Arten. Ging man noch bis vor wenigen Jahren davon aus, dass Hybriden bei Schildkröten nur seltene Zufälle sind, so hat sich der Sachverhalt hier grundlegend geändert, und mit Erscheinen dieses Buchs sind aus der Familie Geoemydidae über 100 verschiedene Hybriden bekannt. Zum einen gibt es da die "künstlichen" Hybriden, d. h. Mischlinge, die durch die Verpaarung bzw. Vergesellschaftung verschiedenster Arten gezielt vom Menschen "geschaffen" werden, speziell in den großen Schildkrötenfarmen Chinas oder bei Hobbyzüchtern. Auf der anderen Seite gibt es aber faszinierenderweise speziell bei asiatischen Sumpfschildkröten der Familie Geoemydidae auch Naturhybriden, d. h. Mischlinge aus freier Wildbahn. Einige dieser Hybriden unterscheiden sich derart von ihren Elternarten, dass Wissenschaftler in den vergangenen beiden Jahrzehnten diverse dieser Hybriden als Arten beschrieben haben, z. B. *Cuora serrata, Mauremys iversoni, Mauremys pritchardi, Ocadia glyphistoma* und *Sacalia pseudocellata*. Teils handelt es sich hier um Wildhybriden, wie z.B. bei *Cuora serrata*, eine Kreuzung zwischen *Pyxidea mouhotii* und *Cistoclemmys galbinifrons;* man nennt dies "Evolution bei der Arbeit" und geht derzeit davon aus, dass es sich um eine Artentstehung vor unseren Augen handelt. Doch weshalb geschieht dies? Vermutlich aufgrund des enormen Drucks, der auf den Wildpopulationen der meisten asiatischen Schildkrötenarten lastet. Massive Absammlung für die Lebensmittelmärkte Chinas und großräumige Habitatzerstörung scheinen der Hauptauslöser hierfür zu sein; die wenigen noch verbleibenden Exemplare verpaaren sich mit allem, was einer Schildkröte ähnelt. Andere Formen wie z. B. *Mauremys iversoni* sind gezielt gezüchtete Hybriden, die die Färbung der in China sehr wertvollen *Pyxiclemmys trifasciata* imitieren sollen und so höhere Preise erzielen als die "Mutterart" *Cathaiemys mutica*, die ihrerseits aber mehr Eier produziert als weibliche *Pyxiclemmys trifasciata*. Was lag also für findige chinesische Geschäftsleute näher, als kurzerhand die beiden gewünschten Eigenschaften in einer "Art" zu vereinen. Hinzu kam die Nachfrage westlicher Wissenschaftler nach neuen, bisher unbekannten Schildkrötenformen und deren Bereitschaft, für solche Tiere hohe Summen zu bezahlen. In menschlicher Obhut wird die Verkreuzung durch die Prägung juveniler Tiere aufeinander begünstigt, wie

In human care, the crossing of species is favored by imprinting juvenile specimens on each other, but may also be facilitated by the joint keeping of female specimens of a variety of species with fairly indiscriminate males of other species, and males of *Pyxiclemmys trifasciata* in particular. It remains an interesting fact, though, that Nature has obviously not erected barriers to keep the Asian species separated, as is commonly the case with other animals and also with chelonians from other continents, be it in the form of geographical barriers, different habitat preferences, or other protective mechanisms.

Hybrids are partly marked by a high degree of variability. It may be that all hatchlings of a clutch of eggs look almost identical to each other, but there may also be specimens whose traits place them between their parent species, or those that tend more towards the one or the other parent. To this variability is added the use of various subspecies of parent taxa that may obviously produce a range of clearly distinct hybrids even though the same parent species may be involved. It is usually quite easy to identify the parent species on morphological grounds, and if doubts persist, modern genetic analyses often provide clues. But even these sophisticated techniques cannot always give final answers, and some natural hybrids have remained enigmatic as to their parentages to this day. The problem is aggravated by the fact that there are even crossbreeds between hybrids. Such a hybrid may stem from the pairing of a hybrid with a "good" species or another hybrid. In doing so, a turtle may be created that is hardly determinable as to the specific identity of its parents. This is impossible in mammals, for example, or other orders of animals where hybrids are usually infertile! In Asian chelonians, however, hybrid females are fertile with no limitations, and males may be partly fertile (usually in crosses between members of different genera) or also completely fertile (usually in crosses between species of the same genus).

As you will see on the following pages, the variability in hybrids is phenomenal. It does not only cross the borders between species and genera, but even involves representatives of continents that are separated by thousands of kilometers, as is the case with *Ocadia sinensis* (Asia) × *Rhinoclemmys pulcherrima* (Central America).

Torsten Blanck

auch die Vergesellschaftung weiblicher Exemplare diverser Arten mit sehr paarungsfreudigen Männchen anderer Arten, speziell z. B. männlichen *Pyxiclemmys trifasciata*.

Interessant ist jedoch, dass die Natur gerade bei den asiatischen Arten keine Barrieren eingebaut hat, wie dies im übrigen Tierreich und auch bei Schildkröten anderer Kontinente sonst eher die Regel ist, sei es durch geographische Barrieren, unterschiedliche Habitatpräferenzen oder andere Schutzmechanismen.

Hybriden zeichnen sich durch eine teils hohe Varianz aus, so gibt es einerseits Tiere aus demselben Gelege, die allesamt identisch aussehen, andererseits aber auch Exemplare aus einem Gelege, die vom Erscheinungsbild her zwischen den Elterntieren stehen sowie Schildkröten, die morphologisch zu einem der Elternteile tendieren. Zu all dieser Varianz kommt noch die Verkreuzung der verschiedensten Unterarten diverser Taxa, die abermals von den typischen Hybriden deutlich abweichende Formen hervorbringen. Meist kann man morphologisch recht einfach die Elternarten entschlüsseln, in anderen Fällen hilft die moderne Genetik, doch auch sie kann nicht alle Fragen klären und wohl auch bei weitem nicht alle natürlichen Kreuzungen entschlüsseln. Erschwerend kommt mittlerweile hinzu, dass es sogar Mischlinge zwischen Hybriden gibt, d. h. ein Hybrid wird mit einer "guten" Art gekreuzt oder gleich mit einem anderen Hybriden. Heraus kommen Formen, deren Ursprung kaum noch nachzuvollziehen ist. Dies ist z. B. bei Säugern und den meisten anderen Tierordnungen nicht möglich. Für gewöhnlich sind Hybriden dort unfruchtbar! Nicht aber so bei asiatischen Schildkröten, wo weibliche Hybriden uneingeschränkt fruchtbar sind und Männchen je nach Hybridform wenigstens teilweise fertil (meist bei Kreuzungen zwischen Angehörigen verschiedener Gattungen) bis ebenfalls komplett fruchtbar (in der Regel bei Kreuzungen zwischen Arten innerhalb einer Gattung) sind.

Wie sie auf den kommenden Seiten sehen werden, ist die Vielfalt der Hybriden gigantisch und überschreitet Art- und Gattungsgrenzen und sogar Kontinente, die viele tausend Kilometer voneinander entfernt sind, z. B. im Falle von *Ocadia sinensis* (Asien) × *Rhinoclemmys pulcherrima* (Mittelamerika).

Torsten Blanck

RTH0001-4 *"Cuora serrata"* Iverson & McCord, 1992

Cistoclemmys galbinifrons × *Pyxidea mouhotii obsti*

photo: S. Szymanski

RTH0012-4 *"Cuora serrata"* Iverson & McCord, 1992

Cistoclemmys galbinifrons group × *Pyxidea mouhotii*

photo: P.P. van Dijk

RTH0003-4 *"Cuora serrata"* Iverson & McCord, 1992

Cistoclemmys galbinifrons group × *Pyxidea mouhotii*

photo: P.P. van Dijk

RTH0004-4 *"Cuora serrata"* Iverson & McCord, 1992

Cistoclemmys galbinifrons × *Pyxidea mouhotii mouhotii*

photo: J.H. Harding

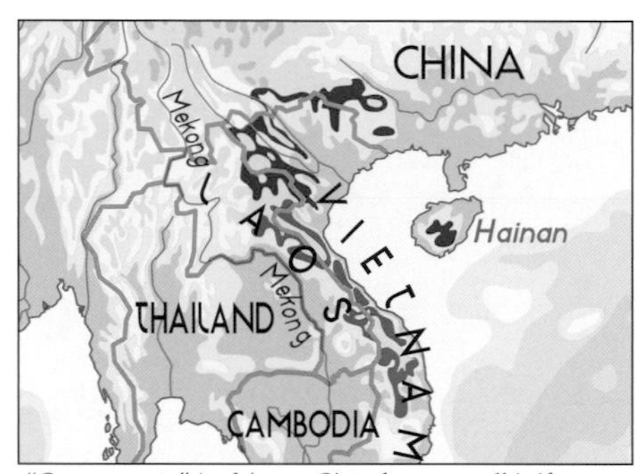

"Cuora serrata" (red/rot = *Cistoclemmys galbinifrons* × *Pyxidea mouhoutii mouhoutii*; blue/blau = *Cistoclemmys bourreti* × *Pyxidea mouhoutii obsti*; green/grün = *Cistoclemmys picturata* × *Pyxidea mouhoutii obsti*)

RTH0005-4 *"Cuora serrata"* Iverson & McCord, 1992

Cistoclemmys galbinifrons × *Pyxidea mouhotii obsti*

photo: P.P. van Dijk

RTH0006-4 *"Cuora serrata"* Iverson & McCord, 1992

Cistoclemmys galbinifrons × *Pyxidea mouhotii mouhotii*

photo: Hou Mian

RTH0007-4 *"Cuora serrata"* Iverson & McCord, 1992

Cistoclemmys bourreti × *Pyxidea mouhotii mouhotii*

photo: Hou Mian

RTH0018-4 *"Cuora serrata"* Iverson & McCord, 1992

Cistoclemmys galbinifrons × *Pyxidea mouhotii mouhotii*

photo: J.B. Iverson

RTH0019-4 *"Cuora serrata"* Iverson & McCord, 1992

Cistoclemmys bourreti × *Pyxidea mouhotii obsti*

photo: B. Esser

RTH0010-4 *"Cuora serrata"* Iverson & McCord, 1992

Cistoclemmys bourreti × *Pyxidea mouhotii obsti*

photo: P.P. van Dijk

RTH001X-4 *"Cuora serrata"* Iverson & McCord, 1992

Cistoclemmys bourreti × *Pyxidea mouhotii obsti*

photo: Hou Mian

RTH0021-4 *"Mauremys iversoni"* PRITCHARD & MCCORD, 1991
Cathaiemys mutica mutica × Pyxiclemmys trifasciata

photo: T. BLANCK

RTH0022-4 *"Mauremys iversoni"* PRITCHARD & MCCORD, 1991
Cathaiemys mutica mutica × Pyxiclemmys trifasciata

photo: J.B. IVERSON

RTH0023-4 *"Mauremys iversoni"* PRITCHARD & MCCORD, 1991
Cathaiemys mutica mutica × Pyxiclemmys trifasciata
♀

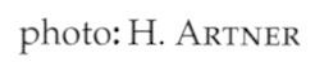

photo: H. ARTNER

RTH0024-1 *"Mauremys iversoni"* PRITCHARD & MCCORD, 1991
Cathaiemys mutica mutica × Pyxiclemmys trifasciata
Hatchling/Schlüpfling

photo: H. ARTNER

RTH0025-4 *"Mauremys iversoni"* PRITCHARD & MCCORD, 1991
Cathaiemys mutica mutica × Pyxiclemmys trifasciata

photo: J.B. IVERSON

RTH0026-4 *"Mauremys iversoni"* PRITCHARD & MCCORD, 1991
Cathaiemys mutica mutica × Pyxiclemmys trifasciata, ♀

photo: T. BLANCK

RTH0031-4 *"Mauremys pritchardi"* McCord, 1997
♀
Cathaiemys mutica mutica × Chinemys reevesii,

photo: U. Jost

RTH0032-4 *"Mauremys pritchardi"* McCord, 1997
♂
Cathaiemys mutica mutica × Chinemys reevesii

photo: U. Jost

RTH0033-4 *"Mauremys pritchardi"* McCord, 1997

Cathaiemys mutica mutica × Chinemys reevesii

photo: T. Blanck

RTH0034-4 *"Mauremys pritchardi"* McCord, 1997
♀
Cathaiemys mutica mutica × Chinemys reevesii

photo: U. Jost

RTH0035-4 *"Mauremys pritchardi"* McCord, 1997
♀
Cathaiemys mutica mutica × Chinemys reevesii

photo: T. Blanck

RTH0036-4 *"Mauremys pritchardi"* McCord, 1997

Cathaiemys mutica mutica × Chinemys reevesii

photo: B. Esser

RTH0037-4 *"Mauremys pritchardi"* McCord, 1997

Cathaiemys mutica mutica × Chinemys reevesii

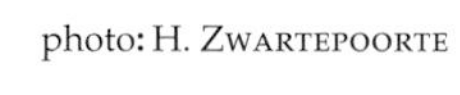

photo: H. Zwartepoorte

RTH0038-4 *"Mauremys pritchardi"* McCord, 1997
♀
Cathaiemys mutica mutica × Chinemys reevesii

photo: T. Blanck

RTH0039-4 *"Mauremys pritchardi"* McCord, 1997

Cathaiemys mutica mutica × Chinemys reevesii

photo: T. Blanck

RTH0041-4 *"Sacalia pseudocellata"* Iverson & McCord, 1992
Pyxiclemmys trifasciata × Sacalia quadriocellata

photo: M. Tang

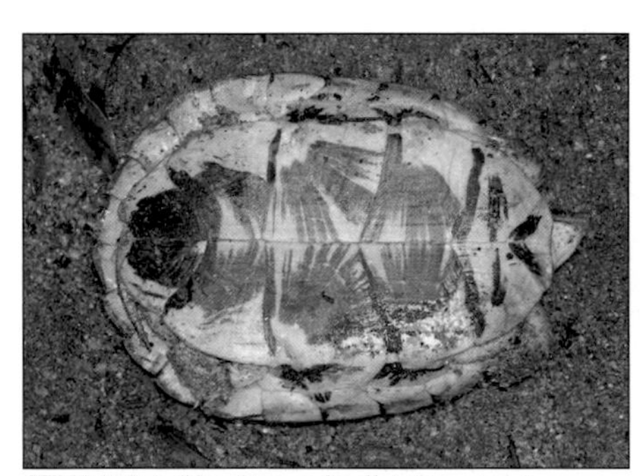

RTH0042-4 *"Sacalia pseudocellata"* Iverson & McCord, 1992
Pyxiclemmys trifasciata × Sacalia quadriocellata

photo: M. Tang

RTH0043-4 *"Sacalia pseudocellata"* Iverson & McCord, 1992
Pyxiclemmys trifasciata × Sacalia quadriocellata

photo: J.B. Iverson

RTH0051-4 *"Ocadia glyphistoma"* McCord & Iverson, 1994
Cathaiemys annamensis × Ocadia sinensis

photo: J.B. Iverson

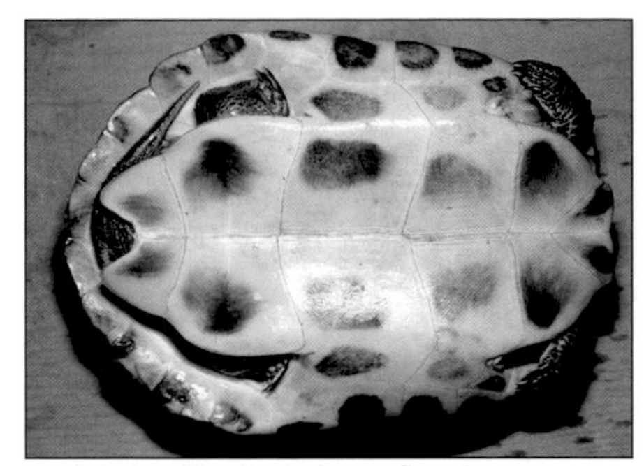

RTH0052-4 *"Ocadia glyphistoma"* McCord & Iverson, 1994
Cathaiemys annamensis × Ocadia sinensis

photo: J.B. Iverson

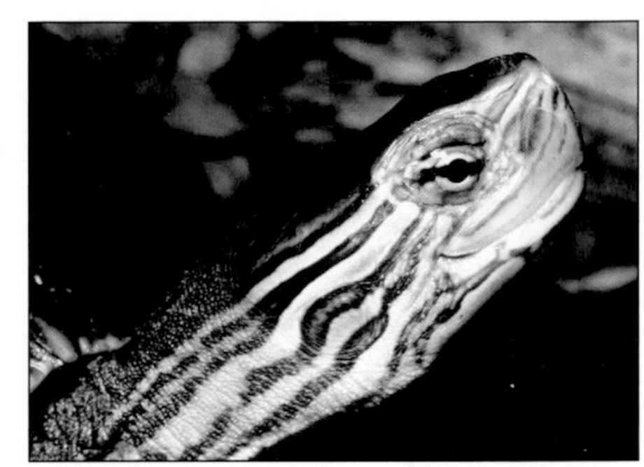

RTH0053-4 *"Ocadia glyphistoma"* McCord & Iverson, 1994
Cathaiemys annamensis × Ocadia sinensis

photo: J.B. Iverson

RTH0061-4 *Ocadia sinensis × Pyxiclemmys trifasciata*

photo: M. Tang

RTH0062-4 *Ocadia sinensis × Pyxiclemmys trifasciata*

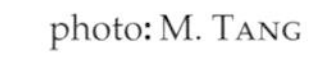

photo: M. Tang

RTH0071-4 *"Ocadia philippeni"* McCord & Iverson, 1992
Ocadia sinensis × Pyxiclemmys trifasciata × Cathaiemys mutica ssp.

photo: J.B. Iverson

RTH0081-4 *Pyxiclemmys trifasciata × Pyxidea mouhotii* ssp.

photo: M. Tang

RTH0082-4 *Pyxiclemmys trifasciata × Pyxidea mouhotii* ssp.

photo: M. Tang

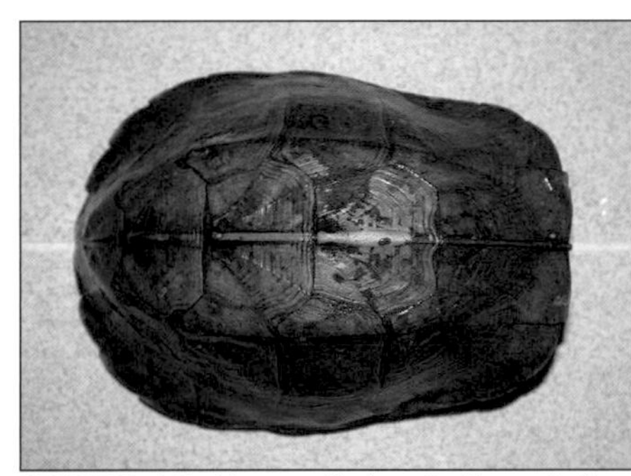

RTH0083-4 *Pyxiclemmys trifasciata × Pyxidea mouhotii* ssp.

photo: M. Tang

RTH0084-4 *Pyxiclemmys trifasciata × Pyxidea mouhotii* ssp.

photo: Zhou Ting

RTH0085-4 *Pyxiclemmys trifasciata × Pyxidea mouhotii* ssp.

photo: Zhou Ting

RTH0086-4 *Pyxiclemmys trifasciata × Pyxidea mouhotii* ssp.

photo: Zhou Ting

RTH0091-4 *Cathaiemys annamensis* × *Cathaiemys mutica* ssp.

photo: T. BLANCK

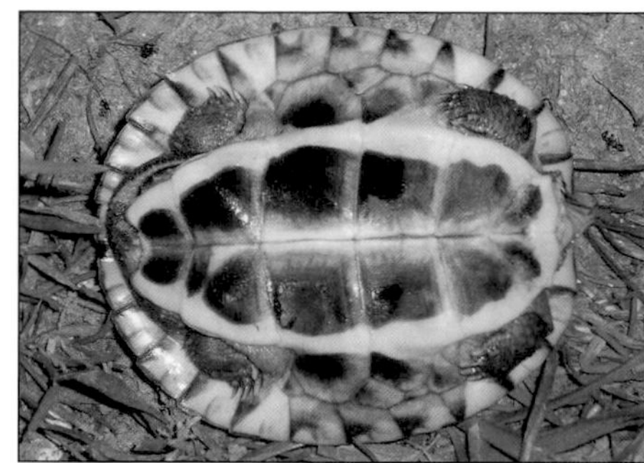
RTH0092-4 *Cathaiemys annamensis* × *Cathaiemys mutica* ssp.

photo: T. BLANCK

RTH0093-4 *Cathaiemys annamensis* × *Cathaiemys mutica* ssp.

photo: N. KAWAZOE/CREEPER

RTH0101-4 *Cathaiemys annamensis* × *Chinemys nigricans* × *Cuora amboinensis* ssp.

photo: T. HONDA

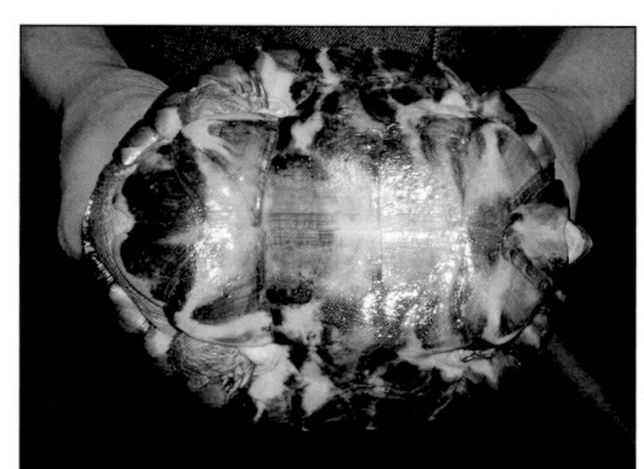
RTH0102-4 *Cathaiemys annamensis* × *Chinemys nigricans* × *Cuora amboinensis* ssp.

photo: T. HONDA

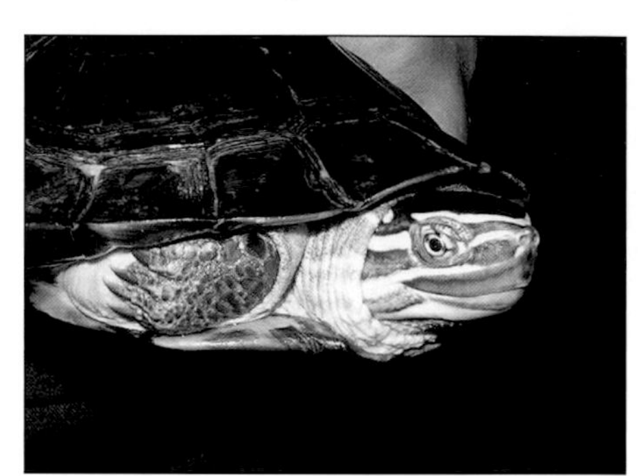
RTH0103-4 *Cathaiemys annamensis* × *Chinemys nigricans* × *Cuora amboinensis* ssp.

photo: T. HONDA

RTH0111-4 *Cathaiemys annamensis* × *Chinemys reevesii*

photo: M. TANG

RTH0112-4 *Cathaiemys annamensis* × *Chinemys reevesii*

photo: M. TANG

RTH0113-4 *Cathaiemys annamensis* × *Chinemys reevesii*

photo: M. TANG

RTH0121-4 *Cathaiemys annamensis* × *Cuora amboinensis* ssp.

photo: P.PETRAS

RTH0122-4 *Cathaiemys annamensis* × *Cuora amboinensis* ssp.

photo: P.PETRAS

RTH0123-4 *Cathaiemys annamensis* × *Cuora amboinensis* ssp.

photo: P.PETRAS

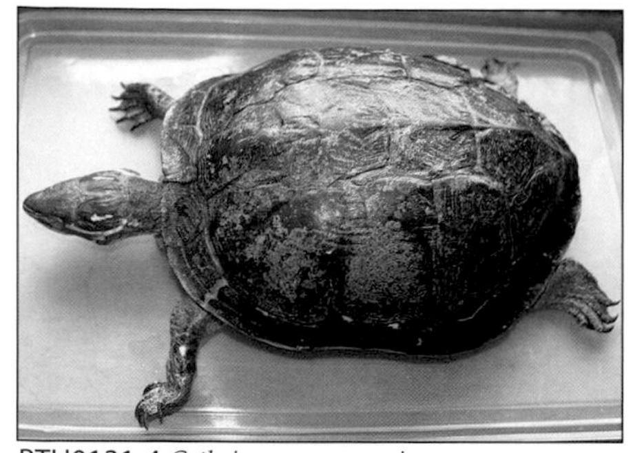
RTH0131-4 *Cathaiemys annamensis* × *Cuora amboinensis* ssp. × *Chinemys reevesii*

photo: Hou Mian

RTH0132-4 *Cathaiemys annamensis* × *Cuora amboinensis* ssp. × *Chinemys reevesii*

photo: Hou Mian

RTH0133-4 *Cathaiemys annamensis* × *Cuora amboinensis* ssp. × *Chinemys reevesii*

photo: Hou Mian

RTH0141-4 *Cathaiemys mutica mutica* × *Ocadia sinensis*

photo: M. Tang

RTH0142-4 *Cathaiemys mutica mutica* × *Ocadia sinensis*

photo: M. Tang

RTH0151-4 *Ocadia japonica* × *Ocadia sinensis*

photo: T. Blanck

RTH0161-4 *Cathaiemys mutica* ssp. (Taiwan) × *Ocadia sinensis*

photo: M. Nesbit

RTH0162-4 *Cathaiemys mutica* ssp. (Taiwan) × *Ocadia sinensis*

photo: M. Nesbit

RTH0163-4 *Cathaiemys mutica* ssp. (Taiwan) × *Ocadia sinensis*

photo: M. Nesbit

RTH0171-4 *Cathaiemys mutica* ssp. × *Cuora amboinensis*

photo: Zhou Ting

RTH0172-4 *Cathaiemys mutica* ssp. × *Cuora amboinensis*

photo: Zhou Ting

RTH0173-4 *Cathaiemys mutica* ssp. × *Cuora amboinensis*

photo: Zhou Ting

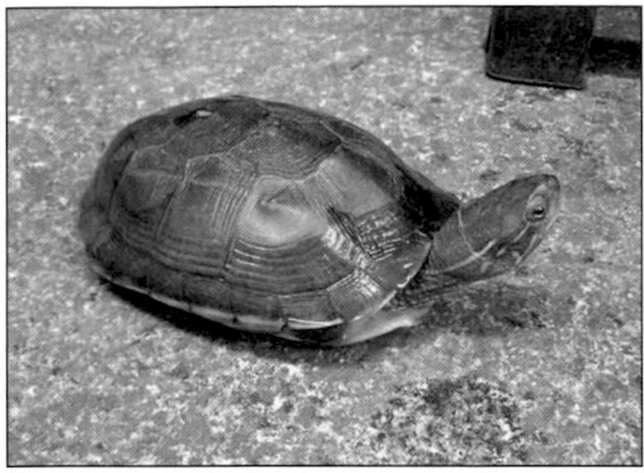

RTH0181-4 *Cathaiemys mutica* ssp. × *Chinemys reevesii*

photo: M. Tang

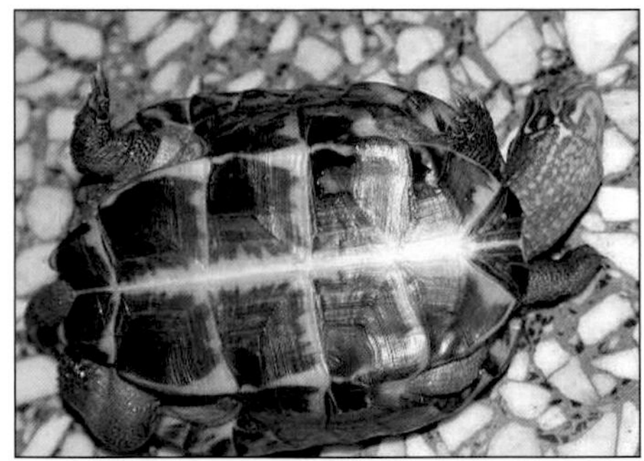

RTH0182-4 *Cathaiemys mutica* ssp. × *Chinemys reevesii*

photo: M. Tang

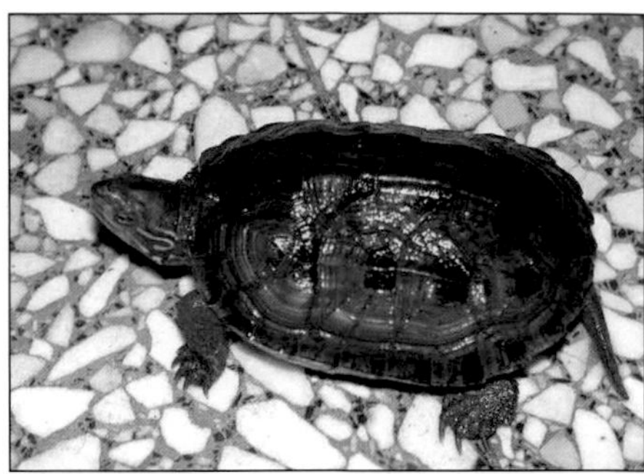

RTH0183-4 *Cathaiemys mutica* ssp. × *Chinemys reevesii*

photo: M. Tang

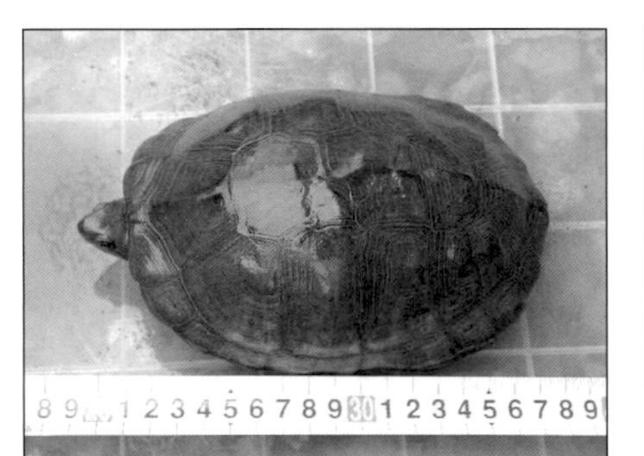

RTH0191-4 *Cathaiemys mutica* ssp. × *Ocadia japonica*

photo: R. Peponi

RTH0192-4 *Cathaiemys mutica* ssp. × *Ocadia japonica*

photo: R. Peponi

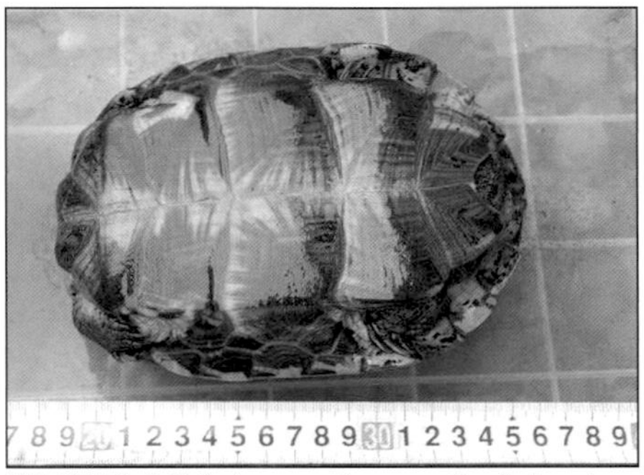

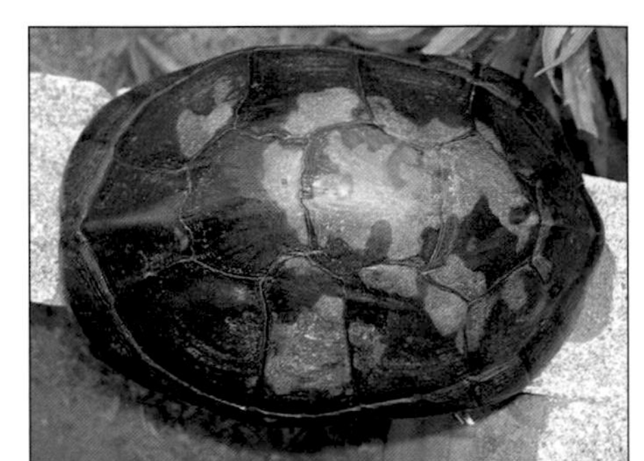

RTH0201-4 *Cathaiemys mutica* ssp. × *Chinemys nigricans*

photo: M. Tang

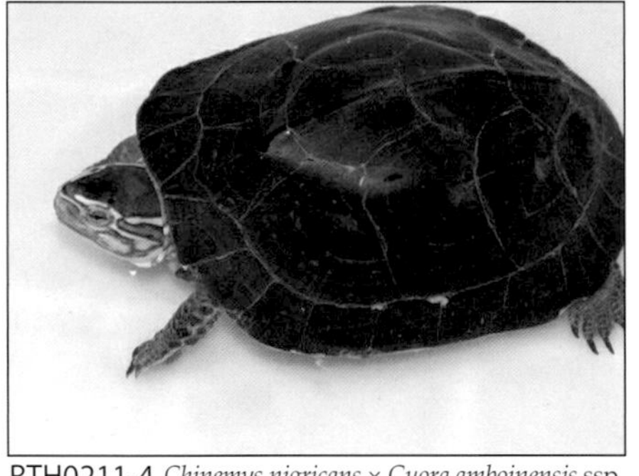

RTH0211-4 *Chinemys nigricans* × *Cuora amboinensis* ssp.

photo: M. Tang

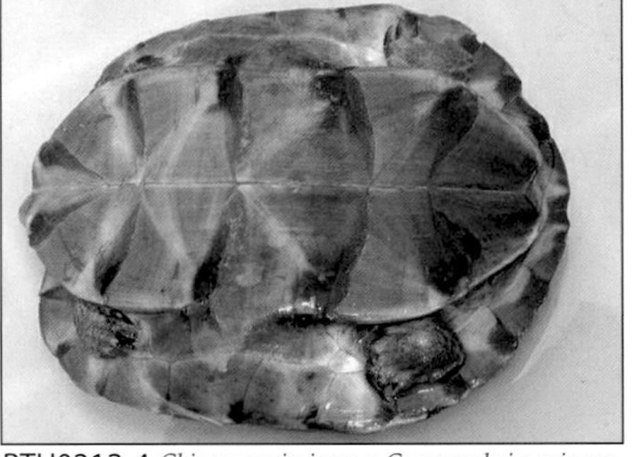

RTH0212-4 *Chinemys nigricans* × *Cuora amboinensis* ssp.

photo: M. Tang

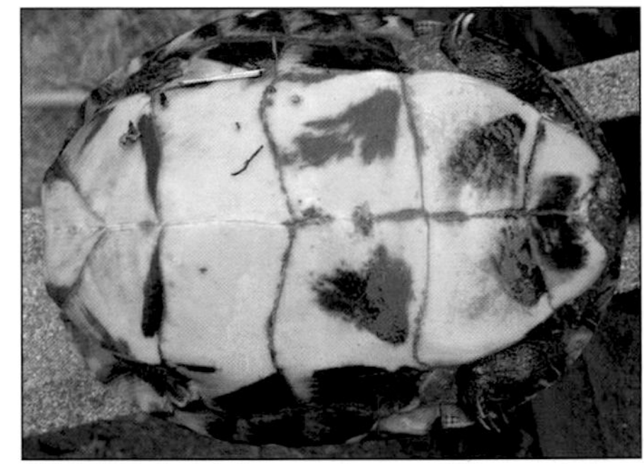

RTH0202-4 *Cathaiemys mutica* ssp. × *Chinemys nigricans*

photo: M. Tang

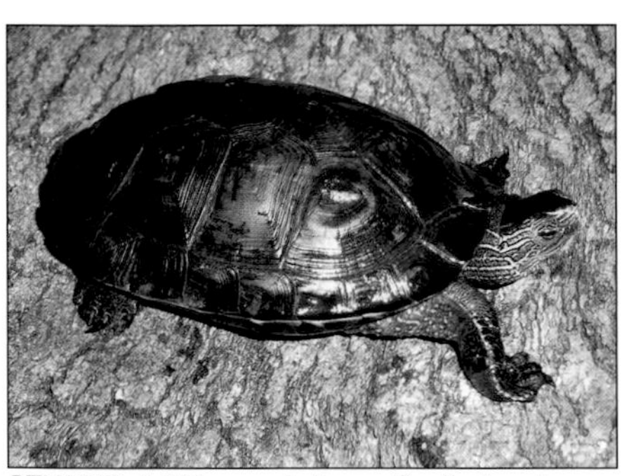

RTH0221-4 *Chinemys nigricans* × *Ocadia sinensis*

photo: T. Blanck

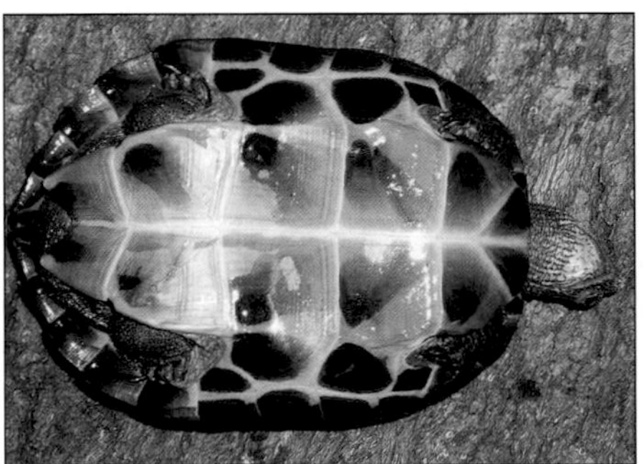

RTH0222-4 *Chinemys nigricans* × *Ocadia sinensis*

photo: T. Blanck

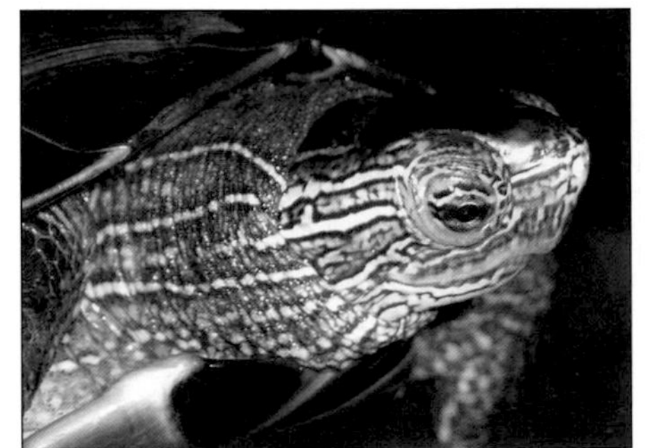

RTH0223-4 *Chinemys nigricans* × *Ocadia sinensis*

photo: T. Blanck

RTH0231-4 *Chinemys reevesii* × *Cistoclemmys flavomarginata* ssp. (animal to the left/linkes Tier; to the right/rechts: *Cistoclemmys flavomarginata* ssp.)

photo: Lin Ying

RTH0232-4 *Chinemys reevesii* × *Cistoclemmys flavomarginata* ssp.

photo: Lin Ying

RTH0233-4 *Chinemys reevesii* × *Cistoclemmys flavomarginata* ssp.

photo: Lin Ying

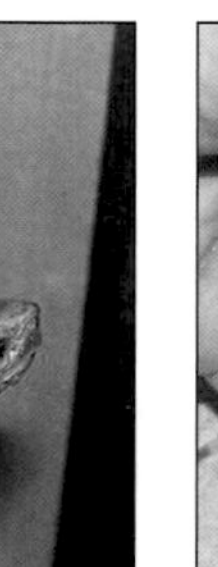

RTH0241-4 *Chinemys reevesii* × *Ocadia japonica*

photo: R. Peponi

RTH0242-4 *Chinemys reevesii* × *Ocadia japonica*

photo: T. Blanck

RTH0243-1 *Chinemys reevesii* × *Ocadia japonica*

photo: R. Peponi

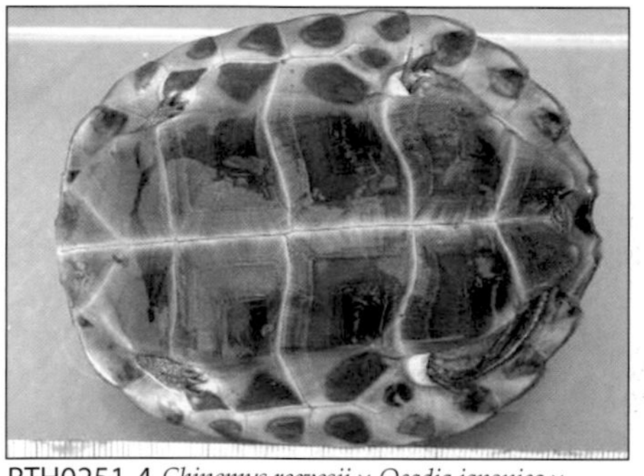

RTH0251-4 *Chinemys reevesii* × *Ocadia japonica* × *Ocadia sinensis*

photo: R. Peponi

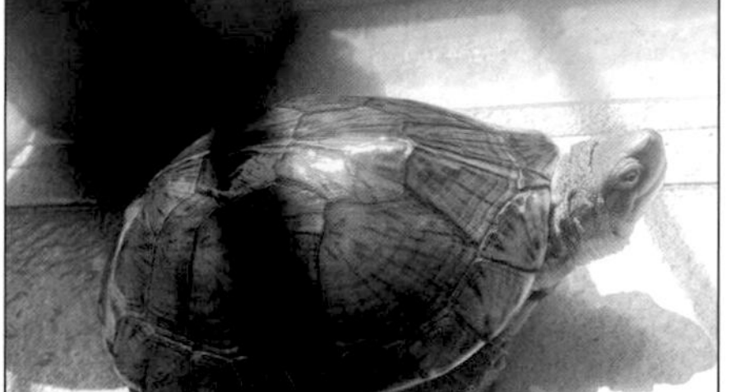

RTH0261-4 *Cathaiemys mutica* ssp. × *Sacalia quadriocellata*

photo: M. Tang

RTH0262-4 *Cathaiemys mutica* ssp. × *Sacalia quadriocellata*

photo: M. Tang

RTH0271-4 *Sacalia quadriocellata* × *Chinemys reevesi*

photo: J.F. Parham

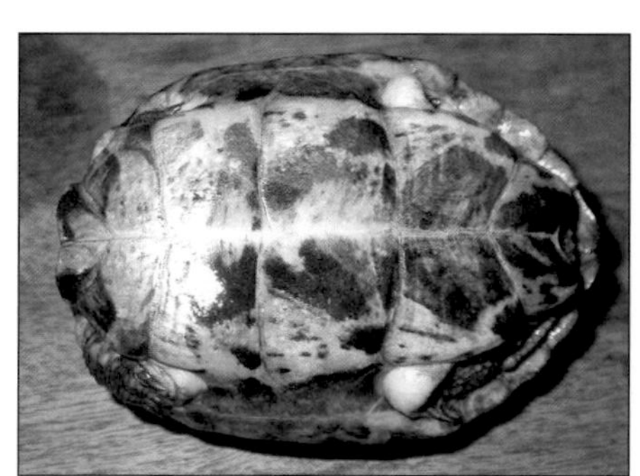

RTH0272-4 *Sacalia quadriocellata* × *Chinemys reevesi*

photo: J.F. Parham

RTH0273-4 *Sacalia quadriocellata* × *Chinemys reevesi*

photo: J.F. Parham

RTH0281-4 *Cistoclemmys flavomarginata* ssp. × *Geoemyda japonica*

photo: N. KAWAZOE/CREEPER

RTH0283-4 *Cistoclemmys flavomarginata* ssp. × *Geoemyda japonica*

photo: N. KAWAZOE/CREEPER

RTH0282-4 *Cistoclemmys flavomarginata* ssp. × *Geoemyda japonica*

photo: N. KAWAZOE/CREEPER

RTH0285-4 *Cistoclemmys flavomarginata* ssp. × *Geoemyda japonica*

photo: HU ZEWEI

RTH0286-4 *Cistoclemmys flavomarginata* ssp. × *Geoemyda japonica*

photo: HU ZEWEI

RTH0284-4 *Cistoclemmys flavomarginata* ssp. × *Geoemyda japonica*

photo: HU ZEWEI

RTH0291-4 *Cuora amboinensis* ssp. × *Malayemys subtrijuga*

photo: M. TANG

RTH0292-4 *Cuora amboinensis* ssp. × *Malayemys subtrijuga*

photo: M. TANG

RTH0293-4 *Cuora amboinensis* ssp. × *Malayemys subtrijuga*

photo: M. TANG

RTH0301-4 *Cuora amboinensis* ssp. × *Pyxiclemmys trifasciata*

photo: H. Zwartepoorte

RTH0302-4 *Cuora amboinensis* ssp. × *Pyxiclemmys trifasciata*

photo: Zhou Ting

RTH0303-4 *Cuora amboinensis* ssp. × *Pyxiclemmys trifasciata*

photo: Zhou Ting

RTH0311-4 *Cuora amboinensis* ssp. × *Siebenrockiella crassicollis*

photo: Hou Mian

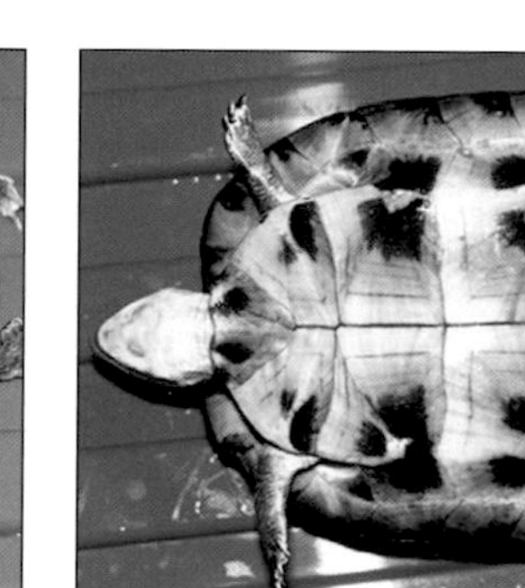

RTH0312-4 *Cuora amboinensis* ssp. × *Siebenrockiella crassicollis*

photo: Hou Mian

RTH0321-4 *Cuora amboinensis* ssp. × *Chinemys reevesi*

photo: F. Galgon

RTH0331-4 *Cyclemys shanensis* ssp. × *Ocadia sinensis*

photo: T. Blanck

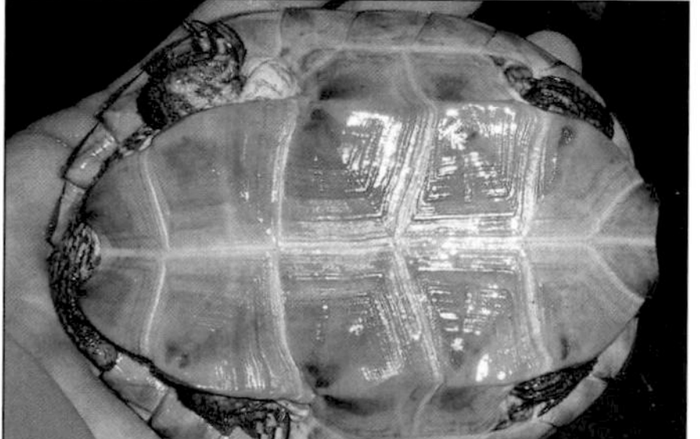

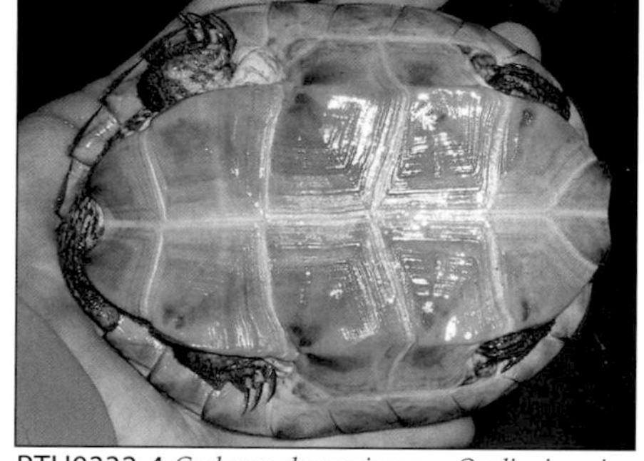

RTH0332-4 *Cyclemys shanensis* ssp. × *Ocadia sinensis*

photo: T. Blanck

RTH0333-4 *Cyclemys shanensis* ssp. × *Ocadia sinensis*

photo: T. Blanck

RTH0341-4 *Cyclemys* sp. × *Melanochelys* sp.

photo: Hou Mian

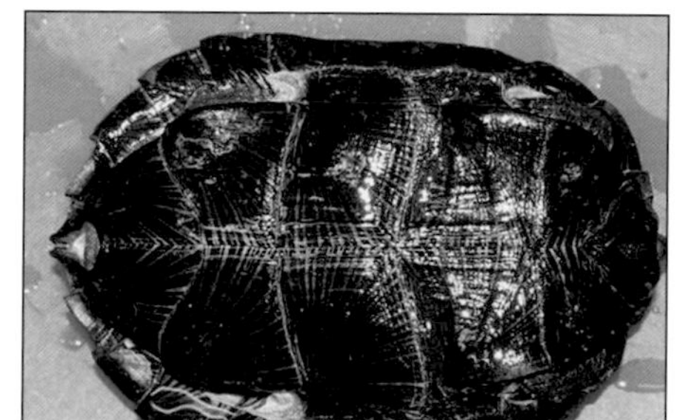

RTH0342-4 *Cyclemys* sp. × *Melanochelys* sp.

photo: Hou Mian

RTH0343-4 *Cyclemys* sp. × *Melanochelys* sp.

photo: Hou Mian

RTH0351-4 *Emmenia rivulata* × *"Mauremys pritchardi"*

photo: T. Blanck

RTH0352-4 *Emmenia rivulata* × *"Mauremys pritchardi"*

photo: T. Blanck

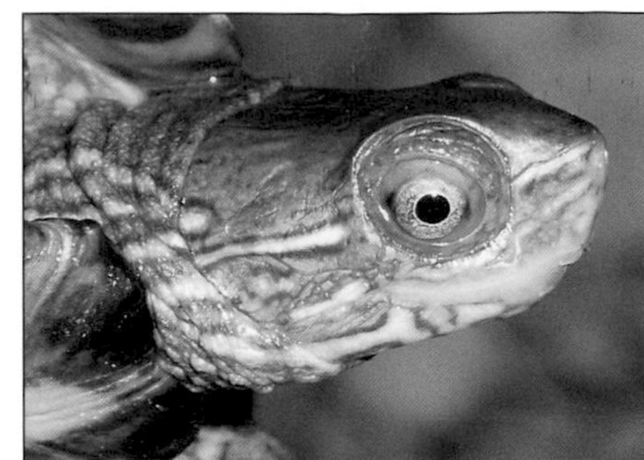

RTH0353-4 *Emmenia rivulata* × *"Mauremys pritchardi"*

photo: T. Blanck

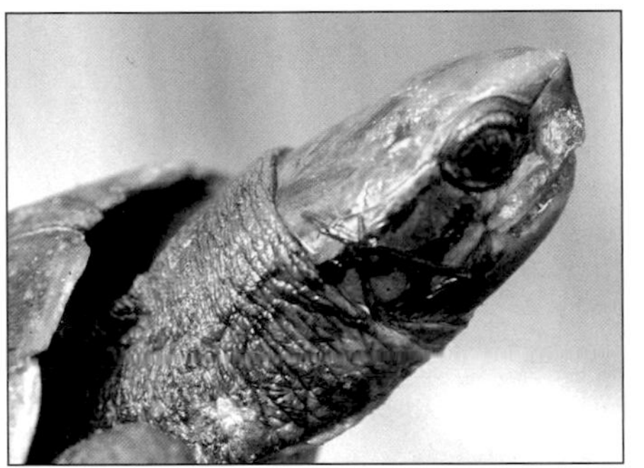

RTH0361-4 *Ocadia japonica* × *Pyxiclemmys trifasciata*

photo: H. Zwartepoorte

RTH0371-4 *Ocadia japonica* × *Rhinoclemmys pulcherrima* ssp.

photo: R. Peponi

RTH0372-4 *Ocadia japonica* × *Rhinoclemmys pulcherrima* ssp.

photo: R. Peponi

RTH0362-4 *Ocadia japonica* × *Pyxiclemmys trifasciata*

photo: H. Zwartepoorte

RTH0381-4 *Ocadia sinensis* × *Rhinoclemmys pulcherrima* ssp.

photo: R. Peponi

RTH0382-4 *Ocadia sinensis* × *Rhinoclemmys pulcherrima* ssp.

photo: R. Peponi

RTH0391-4 *Ocadia sinensis* × *Trachemys scripta* ssp.

photo: Hou Mian

RTH0392-4 *Ocadia sinensis* × *Trachemys scripta* ssp.

photo: Hou Mian

RTH0393-4 *Ocadia sinensis* × *Trachemys scripta* ssp.

photo: Hou Mian

Symbols/*Symbole*

In order to depict as many turtle species and subspecies as possible, and to reckon with the worldwide distribution of our picture volumes, we have decided to do without exhaustive legends, replacing them by international understandable pictograms from which any reader may conclude the basic features and demands of the individual species in husbandry.
Um möglichst alle Schildkröten im Bild zeigen zu können, und um dem weltweiten Vertrieb unserer Bildbände Rechnung zu tragen, haben wir bewusst auf ausführliche Texte verzichtet und ersetzen diese durch international verständliche Symbole, mit deren Hilfe jeder leicht die wichtigsten Eigenschaften der Schildkröten und deren Pflege erkennen kann.

Codenumber/*Codenummer*
The first two numbers denote the animal group; "R" is for "Reptiles, "T" for "Turtles"; each taxon acquires hereby (together with the following five numbers) its distinct codenumber, that remains the same even when systematic status changes. The codenumbers allow international communication. The last figure of the codenumber depicts the age of the animal shown.
Die ersten zwei Buchstaben erläutern die Tiergruppe; "R" steht für "Reptiles", "T" für "Turtles"; zusammen mit den fünf folgenden Zahlen erhält jedes Taxon so seine unverwechselbare Codenummer, die es auch dann behält, wenn sich der systematische Status ändert. Die Codenummern dienen der Verständigung auf internationaler Ebene. Die letzte Ziffer verweist auf das Alter des abgebildeten Tiers:
1 = hatchling/*Schlüpfling*
2 = juvenile/*Jungtier*
3 = subadult/*subadult*
4 = adult/*adult*
5 = very old specimen/*sehr altes Exemplar*

Gender/*Geschlecht*
♂ male/*männlich*, ♀ female/*weiblich*, ♂♀ couple/*Paar*

Size/*Größe*
in cm = the approx. straight carapace length the turtles can achieve as adults/
in cm = ungefähre Carapaxlänge (Stockmaß; nicht über die Panzerwölbung gemessen), die die Schildkröten als Adulti erreichen können

Terrarium Size/*Terrariengröße*
Minimum size of terrarium for 1–2 turtles (CL = Straight carapace length); add 20 % of space for each additional specimen/Mindestgröße Terrarium für 1–2 Schildkröten (CL = Stockmaß Carapaxlänge); für jedes weitere Exemplar 20 % Grundfläche zusätzlich

S	Length/*Länge* = CL x 4	Width/*Breite* = CL x 2
M	Length/*Länge* = CL x 6	Width/*Breite* = CL x 3
L	Length/*Länge* = CL x 8	Width/*Breite* = CL x 4
XL	Length/*Länge* = CL x 20	Width/*Breite* = CL x 10

Water Level/*Wasserstand*
medium, shell width x 3/*mittel, Panzerbreite x 3*
high, shell width x 5/*hoch, Panzerbreite x 5*

Settings/*Behältereinrichtung*
arid: sand, earth, stones, roots, water dish/
trocken: Sand, Erde, Steine, Wurzeln, Trinkgefäß
semi-humid: sphagnum, earth, dead leaves, stones, roots, large water basin (land section 70 %, *water section 30 %; water level: carapace height x 0,5)/*
halbfeucht: Torfmoos, Erde, Laub, Steine, Wurzeln, großes Wasserbecken (Landteil 70 %, Wasserteil 30 %; Wasserstand Panzerhöhe x 0,5)
humid: sphagnum, earth, dead leaves, stones, roots, very large water basin (land section 50 %, water section 50 %; water level: shell width)/
feucht: Torfmoos, Erde, Laub, Steine, Wurzeln, sehr großes Wasserbecken (Landteil 50 %, Wasserteil 50 %; Wasserstand Panzerbreite)

water basin with stones, roots and plastic plants as submersed hiding places/
Wasserteil mit Steinen, Wurzeln und Plastikpflanzen als Unterwasserverstecke
high layer of fine sand in the water basin/
hohe feinkörnige Sandschicht im Wasserteil
thin layer of gravel or coarse sand in the water basin/
dünne Kies- oder grobkörnige Sandschicht im Wasserteil
thin layer of fine sand in the water basin/
dünne feinkörnige Sandschicht im Wasserteil
land section mainly for oviposition/
Landteil hauptsächlich zur Eiablage
land section for oviposition and basking/
Landteil für Eiablage und Sonnenbäder
S specialist: rock crevices as hiding places/
Spezialist: Felsspalten als Unterschlupf
<Sw> specialist: saltwater dweller/
Spezialist: Salzwasserbewohner

Temperature (at least 23–26 °C at daytime)/
Temperatur (tagsüber mindestens 23–26 °C)
no additional radiation heat required/
keine zusätzliche Strahlungswärme erforderlich
35°C radiation heat required locally up to approx. 35 °C/
Strahlungswärme lokal bis ca. 35 °C
45°C radiation heat required locally up to approx. 45 °C/
Strahlungswärme lokal bis ca. 45 °C

Diet/*Ernährung*
mainly carnivorous/*überwiegend Fleischfresser*
mainly herbivorous/*überwiegend Pflanzenfresser*
omnivorous/*Allesfresser*

Periods of Rest/*Ruheperioden*
hibernation at 4–8 °C/*Winterruhe bei 4–8 °C*
in winter, reduced activity at lower temperatures/
im Winter reduzierte Aktivität bei abgesenkten Temperaturen
no hibernation/*keine Winterruhe*

Outdoor husbandry/*Freilandhaltung*
recommendable/*empfehlenswert*
possible at high temperatures/
bei hohen Temperaturen möglich
not recommendable/*nicht empfehlenswert*

Group composition/*Vergesellschaftung*
0 separation of genders recommended/
Geschlechtertrennung empfohlen
1 solitary husbandry recommended/*Einzelhaltung empfohlen*
2 ♂♀
3 ♂♀♀
4 ♂♂♀♀

Peculiarities/*Besonderheiten*
suitable for beginners as well/*auch für Anfänger geeignet*
attention: suitable for experienced keepers only/
Vorsicht, nur für erfahrene Halter geeignet
protected species (CITES and/or EU regulations)/
geschützte Art (CITES und/oder EU)

available:

Vol. 1: Europe, Africa and Western Asia, 2002, 96 pages, 450 color pictures

lieferbar:

Bd. 1: Europa, Afrika und Westasien, 2002, 96 Seiten, 450 Farbfotos

available:

Vol. 2: North America, 2004, 127 pages, more than 500 color pictures, 40 color distribution maps

lieferbar:

Bd. 2: Nordamerika, 2004, 127 Seiten, über 500 Farbfotos, 40 farbige Verbreitungskarten

available:

Vol. 3: Central and South America, 2005, 128 pages, more than 600 color pictures, 40 color distribution maps

lieferbar:

Bd. 3: Mittel- und Südamerika, 2005, 128 Seiten, über 600 Farbfotos, 40 farbige Verbreitungskarten

In preparation/In Vorbereitung:

- Vol. 5: Australia and Oceania (spring 2007)
- Bd. 5: Australien und Ozeanien (Frühjahr 2007)

RUSSIAN F
Tyumen'
Yekaterinburg
Kurgan
Omsk
Novosibirsk
Tomsk
Kemerovo
Petropavlosk
Kustanay
Ishim
Tobol
Kokshetau
Ozero Siletiteniz
Irtysh
Barnaul
Gorno-Altaysk
ASTANA
Ozero Tengiz
Semipalatinsk
Karaganda
Ust'-Kamenogorsk
Uvs Nuur
Volga
Ural'sk
Aktyubinsk
Don
KAZAKHSTAN
Ozero Zaysan
Har Us Nuur
Atyrau
CASPIAN SEA
Aral Sea
Ozero Balkhash
Taldykorgan
Ozero Alakol'
Shihezi
Urumqi
Yining
Kyzylorda
Alma-Ata
BISHKEK
Ysyk-Köl
Taraz
UZBEKISTAN
Nukus
Shymkent
KYRGYZSTAN
Zaliv Kara-Bogaz Gol
Urgench
Namangan
Andizan
Osh
Bosten Hu
SINKIANG
Lop Nur
TURKMENIA
TASHKENT
Khujand
Kashi
Kaxgar He
Turkmenbashi
Samarkand
Turkmenabat
TAJIKISTAN
ASHKHABAD
Mary
DUSHANBE
Mazar-e Sharif
Mashhad
KABUL
Indus
Srinagar
KASHMIR
Herat
Peshawar
ISLAMABAD
AFGHANISTAN
Faisalabad
Lahore
CH
TIBET
Kandahar
Sutlej
Chandigarh
Lhasa
Quetta
Multan
DELHI
NEPAL
Brahmaputra
PAKISTAN
New Delhi
KATHMANDU
BHUTAN
THIMPHU
Jodhpur
Jaipur
Lucknow
Persian Gulf
Indus
Kanpur
Ganges
Hyderabad
INDIA
Varanasi
Patna
Guwahati
Karachi
BANGLADESH
Gandhinagar
Ahmadabad
Bhopal
Calcutta
DACCA
Rajkot
Vadodara
Narmada
Indore
Porbandar
Nagpur
Mahanadi
Surat
Durg
Bhubaneshwar
Sittwe
Bay of Bengal
Bombay
Godavari
Sholapur
Vishakhapatnam
RANGOON
ARABIAN SEA
Hyderabad
Krishna
Panaji
Madras
Gulf of Aden
Lakshadweep Islands INDIA
Bangalore
Pondicherry
Cochin
Madurai
Jaffna
Trivandrum
SRI LANKA
Nicobar Islands INDIA
COLOMBO
Galle
MALDIVES
MALE
EQUATOR

Symbols/*Symbole*

In order to depict as many turtle species and subspecies as possible, and to
picture volumes, we have decided to do without exhaustive legends, replaci
tograms from which any reader may conclude the basic features and demanc
Um möglichst alle Schildkröten im Bild zeigen zu können, und um dem weltweiter
haben wir bewusst auf ausführliche Texte verzichtet und ersetzen diese durch int
jeder leicht die wichtigsten Eigenschaften der Schildkröten und deren Pflege erke

Codenumber/*Codenummer*

The first two numbers denote the animal group; "R" is for "Reptiles, "T" for "Turtles"; each taxon acquires hereby (together with the following five numbers) its distinct codenumber, that remains the same even when systematic status changes. The codenumbers allow international communication. The last figure of the codenumber depicts the age of the animal shown.
Die ersten zwei Buchstaben erläutern die Tiergruppe; "R" steht für "Reptiles", "T" für "Turtles"; zusammen mit den fünf folgenden Zahlen erhält jedes Taxon so seine unverwechselbare Codenummer, die es auch dann behält, wenn sich der systematische Status ändert. Die Codenummern dienen der Verständigung auf internationaler Ebene. Die letzte Ziffer verweist auf das Alter des abgebildeten Tiers:

1 = hatchling/*Schlüpfling*
2 = juvenile/*Jungtier*
3 = subadult/*subadult*
4 = adult/*adult*
5 = very old specimen/*sehr altes Exemplar*

Gender/*Geschlecht*

♂ male/*männlich*, ♀ female/*weiblich*, ♂♀ couple/*Paar*

Size/*Größe*

in cm = the approx. straight carapace length the turtles can achieve as adults/
in cm = ungefähre Carapaxlänge (Stockmaß; nicht über die Panzerwölbung gemessen), die die Schildkröten als Adulti erreichen können

Terrarium Size/*Terrariengröße*

Minimum size of terrarium for 1–2 turtles (CL = Straight carapace length); add 20 % of space for each additional specimen/Mindestgröße Terrarium für 1–2 Schildkröten (CL = Stockmaß Carapaxlänge); für jedes weitere Exemplar 20 % Grundfläche zusätzlich

S	Length/*Länge* = CL x 4	Width/*Breite* = CL x 2
M	Length/*Länge* = CL x 6	Width/*Breite* = CL x 3
L	Length/*Länge* = CL x 8	Width/*Breite* = CL x 4
XL	Length/*Länge* = CL x 20	Width/*Breite* = CL x 10

Water Level/*Wasserstand*

medium, shell width x 3/*mittel, Panzerbreite x 3*
high, shell width x 5/*hoch, Panzerbreite x 5*

Settings/*Behältereinrichtung*

arid: sand, earth, stones, roots, water dish/
trocken: Sand, Erde, Steine, Wurzeln, Trinkgefäß

semi-humid: sphagnum, earth, dead leaves, stones, roots, large water basin (land section 70 %, *water section 30 %; water level: carapace height x 0,5)/*
halbfeucht: Torfmoos, Erde, Laub, Steine, Wurzeln, großes Wasserbecken (Landteil 70 %, Wasserteil 30 %; Wasserstand Panzerhöhe x 0,5)

humid: sphagnum, earth, dead leaves, stones, roots, very large water basin (land section 50 %, water section 50 %; water level: shell width)/
feucht: Torfmoos, Erde, Laub, Steine, Wurzeln, sehr großes Wasserbecken (Landteil 50 %, Wasserteil 50 %; Wasserstand Panzerbreite)

water ba
as subm
Wasserte
Unterwa
high lay
hohe fei
thin laye
dünne K
thin lay
dünne f
land se
Landtei
land se
Landtei
S speciali
Spezial
<Sw> special
Spezial

Temperatu
Temperatu
no add
keine z
35°C radiati
Strahl
45°C radiat
Strahl

Diet/*Ernä*
mainl
mainl
omni

Periods o
hiber
in wi
im W
no h

Outdoor
reco
poss
bei h
not

Group c
0 sep
Ges
1 soli
2 ♂♀
3 ♂♀
4 ♂♂

Peculia
suit
att
Vor
 prc
ge